Jack McAfghan's
RETURN
From
RAINBOW BRIDGE
Book 3

By Kate McGahan

OTHER BOOKS BY KATE McGAHAN:

Jack McAfghan:
Reflections on Life with my Master

The Lizard from Rainbow Bridge

Only Gone From Your Sight: Jack
McAfghan's Little Guide to Pet Loss & Grief

It's Not Putting Me Down It's Lifting Me Up
(excerpts from the above book)

Only Gone From Your Sight: A Personal
Approach to Human Loss & Grief

One Heart's Journey:
Lyrics of an Imperfect Life

c. 2016 by Kate McGahan
All rights reserved.
ISBN 978-0-9962606-3-3
Printed in the United States of America

DEDICATION

*I dedicate this book to my Jacklight Angels.
These earth angels found each other in the
depths of grief when they connected on
Jack's Pet Loss Facebook Group. They
believed in his message and now spurred
on by a higher cause, they work together to
spread Jack's wisdom to help open minds
and hearts and to bring comfort to those
who grieve. This dedication is my humble
way of thanking them for their love, loyalty
and support.*
*Never be afraid to make a new friend
because you never know what they will
come to mean to you.*

Grief is an emotional rollercoaster.
You will have your ups and downs
And moments of terror
And brief moments of peace.
You can only go as fast
As the ride will take you.
Just remember:
It will end and you will be okay.
Love,
Jack

Dear Reader,

It is not my intention to persuade you to believe in anything you don't already believe in. I strive only to help you to find the inherent faith that is buried deep down inside, hidden beneath the burden of your grief...a faith that makes you stronger than you seem to think you are. I seek only to teach you what to expect from the process of grieving and to share the story of what can happen when you allow miracles to come into your life.

Our story is your story too. The best friend who inspired you to read this book will be right here beside you in the pages ahead, waiting for you to open your heart so that you can read with understanding and further open your mind and connect with your loved one too.

I highly recommend that you read "Jack McAfghan: Reflections on Life with my Master" before embarking on this part of the journey. You will enjoy this sequel much more if you do, for our first book lays the foundation for working through your own grief as it prepares you for this guided journey, which follows. Love never dies and nothing is ever lost that love remembers.

~~The End~~

The Beginning

* Denial *

I've been watching over her one year six months in Earth Time. I have witnessed her tears and the depths of her sadness. For nights on end I have endured her loneliness and despair in the times when she felt I had forsaken her. In vain I have reached out to her when she felt most alone. There were times she didn't believe she could go on living. But she did. Humans do. She is only human after all.

She rescued me from the puppy mill when I was twelve weeks of age and she then trained me and shaped me into the dog I was destined to be. That's what a good master does. Meanwhile I was training, shaping and teaching her too!

We worked the world of hospice together until one fateful day when the vet found a mass inside of me that needed to be surgically removed. I did not recover from the surgery and four days later, I made my Transition, at home on our kitchen floor with her beside me.

For weeks and months afterwards she grieved my loss. She couldn't hear me. She couldn't see me. Yet I was with her all the time. I spoke to her, my heart to hers waiting for her heart to respond to mine.

Grief is a very personal thing, but it has a fairly predictable course. First she had to go through the Denial Phase. She was in shock, much like someone involved in a serious accident who keeps saying, 'this can't be happening. This can't be happening to me'. It's part of grief. It's an involuntary survival tactic.

She went into hibernation, living life on autopilot. Her sleeping habits were all mixed up. She found herself sleeping many hours a day yet waking up tired. She was weary in body and thought all the time. She needed an escape from her tormenting thoughts and her grief but there was no escape. There were nights she could not sleep at all because living with grief is exhausting and she would become very restless and too tired even for sleep.

At times she could imagine that it was all just a bad dream. She convinced herself that she would awaken and we would still be together. It would take her some time to understand that we are still together, for humans seem to need to see, hear or touch something to know that it is real. For this reason we find creative ways to reach out to you from the other side so that you can sense us there. We are always together in another realm. We always have been and we always will be.

Finding Grady

She had graduated college, landed a great job, had a nice car, found a handsome boyfriend and she had just bought her first house. Life was pretty good, but something was missing. She didn't know what.

It could have been that her boyfriend drank too much, for a person who drinks tends to put their love and need for alcohol before their love for their partner.

One day, her outspoken friend Barbara gave her a pep talk. Barbara didn't like the boyfriend. She had Kate's best interests at heart and she never minced her words.

"If you want a puppy why don't you get yourself a dog?"

Kate laughed off the comment but the seed had been planted. A few weeks later she started browsing the classifieds to get an idea what kinds of dogs were available in the area. She called a few of the ads but she either didn't like the sound of the owner or the dog simply didn't feel right to her.

As she was reading through the neighborhood circular, her eyes landed on an ad, "One Year Old Collie-Shepherd Free To A Good Home". She tore the ad out of the paper and proceeded to use it for a bookmark, thinking nothing more about it. It was just something to mark her place.

One Saturday morning a few weeks later, Barbara left Kate a message on her voicemail.

"There's a local breeder who just had a bunch of collie pups! You might want to give him a call," and she left the number. She made it very easy for Kate.

Kate thought about it. She always loved collies. In fact as a child she had been so loyal to Lassie that she refused to watch any other station but CBS when she was growing up. Loyalty has its limits and she still had a lot to learn.

"I don't think I really want a purebred collie," she commented. After a few moments, she remembered the newsprint bookmark and she went to get it out of the book.

"'Free To A Good Home'. Now that's more my style."

She dialed the local number. The lady answered. They lived fifteen minutes away.

"She's a sweetie," the lady said.

Kate got into her car, drove to the trailer park and found her way to the address she'd been given. There, chained to the front corner of a singlewide trailer in grave disrepair, was Grady. She was beautiful. In fact, she looked a lot like Lassie!

"Heyyy! Are you the little girl who needs a home?" she warmly asked Grady as she got out of the car and approached. "Wow. Look at you! You are beautiful!"

Grady proceeded to drop to the ground, onto her back in total joy, her legs flailing in the air. Grady then proceeded to pee all over herself. Kate took a sobering step back.

"Oh. Maybe this is why you are free to a good home..." She had never experienced submissive behavior before. Her childhood dogs were well trained, confident and disciplined.

The owners came outside to meet her and they answered her questions. They were getting rid of Grady because they simply had too many animals. The park manager had issued a notice giving them the choice to remove some of them or be evicted. They had cats (too many to count), and gerbils. Canaries were flying freely through the house. Another old dog that they had decided to keep looked quite sickly, by the name of Jed. The house had broken windows with torn screens, fleas and houseflies. Kate's feet stuck to the carpet inside. Grady was not housebroken. The people were nice but it was pretty clear they didn't have time to spend training her. Grady went home with Kate that day, the boyfriend was forgotten and the rest is history.

The point I want to make is that when two souls are destined to be together, nothing gets in the way. It may take a long time to come into being, but once it comes, it usually happens pretty fast and very easily.

It was already unconditional. It didn't matter to Kate that Grady wasn't housebroken and that she peed all over herself. Grady was the right dog for her. Kate was the right human for Grady. Kate trained her well and Grady never peed in their house. They lived together for fifteen years before Grady transitioned over Rainbow Bridge and into Heaven.

Joey: The Back Up Plan

I didn't mention Joey in my first book because when someone you love is dying it's already complicated enough. The heart and soul can only take in so much information when it is in pain. If you've read my first book, I know you are feeling better, so I'll share our story of Joey with you now.

The days were passing faster and faster. Sensing that my time with her was coming to an end, I knew how important it was for her to have a best friend at her side. I knew it would be easier for me to leave knowing that she wasn't alone. It was time to put the backup plan in place and it was in my power to make it happen.

She always wanted me to be happy, so I would always try to show her what made me happy. I put a plan into effect when she and I went on a cross-country road trip to New York State. We made sure to stop at many dog parks along the way to break up the miles.

I was always very social with everyone. I loved big dogs, little dogs, cats, horses, two-legged and four-legged alike. She was always one to have big dogs and at ninety pounds I was the biggest yet.

On this trip, I made a point of playing with the little dogs. She never had much use for little dogs. She would say to me when we saw them, "Those aren't 'real' dogs!" But I knew they were real. When she told me this, I knew I had something else to teach her. So when we stopped at the various dog parks along the interstate, I made a point of showing her all the little dogs and how much I loved them! I was planting a seed that would eventually grow inside her heart.

My time on earth was winding down. Changes were coming and I wanted her to be prepared too. The Divine Plan was already in place. I saw Joey's face in my mind but I didn't yet know how it would come about. I didn't know how we would find him but I knew that it would happen, sooner or later.

She found herself thinking about little dogs all the way home. It started in Tulsa when she met the cutest little old Pomeranian at the dog park there. She realized that I was getting older and that maybe a lightweight companion would be good for me. She would do anything to keep me alive and well as long as possible.

My plan was working! A few days after we arrived home in Sedona she went online where she saw a little terrier-mix named Joey. Oh he was cute! She thought nothing of driving the hour or so the following day to go to see him.

Joey had been rescued from a kill shelter just hours before he was scheduled to be euthanized. Found wandering alone in the desert, he had been labeled a stray. Even though he was micro-chipped, he went unclaimed. Not only was he tangled, matted and dirty, he was scratched up from the cactus and who knows what else. He was anxious and afraid of many things. It didn't make sense, he was so cute and loving, but everything makes sense once you have the full story.

By the time we met him, he had been groomed, had a clean bill of health and was ready to go. He had many fears, but he was not afraid of me and he sure was not afraid of her! The moment he saw her, he looked up at her with his big dark eyes and he told her how much he loved her. He told her he wanted her. He picked her. She thought she was choosing him but he was choosing her. It was love at first sight and from that moment on, forever and ever, nothing else mattered to him but her.

She felt his feelings reflected in her own heart and that night she brought him home with us, for who can resist being loved, heart and soul? He came joyfully and eagerly. He was all of nine pounds but he was full of love and determination and those two qualities are stronger than any other combination.

The little guy settled in fairly quickly. We often joked with each other that he must be an "Afghan Terrier" because he looked so much like me. People would smile as they passed us on the street and they couldn't help but ask, "Is that her puppy?" They assumed I was Joey's Mommy. It was pretty funny.

I was the older one of the two of us and much more mature so even though I modeled the very best behavior, I would pretty much let Joey have his way with things. I always felt that if two are competing or in a disagreement, the one that should give in is the one who is the most evolved and wise. That would be me.

I saw my karma unfolding before my very eyes. We indeed get what we have given. I used to want her all to myself and she could hardly get a moment with Grady after I came along. Poor Grady! She had been an only "child" for many years. How hard it must have been for her! Now, Joey's eager body would lunge and jump at her, bouncing higher and higher with his love. He was always putting himself in between the two of us. I would look over at her, my eyes meeting hers. Her eyes would say *I'm sorry Jack.* Her mouth would say, "You're still my number one." Her heart said, *I love you I love you.* I would then look back at her and my eyes would say to her, *I had it coming* and my heart would reply, *I love you I love you too.*

I would watch him fight for her and clamor all over her and realize how much he still had to learn. He was just as jealous as I was and even more possessive. He wanted to watch her, be with her, all the time. He tried to stake his claim. I knew it was because he had abandonment issues, but's kind of hard to understand those with abandonment issues until you've walked in their paws.

It was hard for me to not be jealous of him with her because for quite some time she had been mine and mine alone. She was sensitive to this and she always made sure that she gave me a little more attention than she gave to him. She would fix her steady loving gaze on me while ruffling his little furry body and speak in a voice that he could not hear, her heart to mine, in the silent language of love that I taught her to speak. She always reassured me that no one would ever take my place with her. I knew beyond a doubt that I was loved.

It was all good. Joey was the backup plan. I did not want to leave her without someone to love and care for, who loved her in return. Joey couldn't help it. His purpose on earth was to watch over and protect her, for he was an angel too.

Love Takes Time

She did not know that I was her Heart And Soul dog until I was long out of housebreaking and obedience training. Before then I was just a clumsy, silly puppy like so many other puppies. She had plenty of frustration during the training period. Everyone does. Sometimes frustration can get in the way of your feelings of love for someone. You wonder how you can do it another day. But we worked together, we learned to communicate with one another and things straightened out. I learned to know what she expected of me and as I got a little older I learned how to discipline myself and (sort of) control my spontaneous antics. It was then that she could see me clearly as I was...and it was good.

Little angel or not, life was far from ideal with Joey. He was just so cute and he seemed perfect, for the first 24 hours at our house. The truth always comes out when you live with someone day after day.

Very early on, we had to teach him how to tell us when he needed to go to the bathroom. He wouldn't just "go" on the carpets or the floor in one small puddle. Oh no, that would be too easy. He would climb onto beds and couches and pee wildly all over them.

We always wondered how it was that he could be a year old and not yet be housebroken. I knew that it was due in part to him wanting to take over our house. Sure maybe he was nine pounds and I was ninety, but size just doesn't matter with such things. He wanted to be boss. I was blessed, I guess, to have a small ego. I was confident enough, made confident by her love for me. I never cared about having control or needing to be right. He wanted her full attention and to heck with me! He thought she could smell him like dogs smell each other and he wanted her to think about him all the time, so that's why he peed everywhere so that everywhere she went she would think about him all the time. She did think about him, but it was just because she was going crazy watching him and cleaning up after him.

Finally Joey was housebroken. It took quite a long time. She went through a strange phase with him. She had never been anything but loving to me, but she was very impatient with Joey. Sometimes she even regretted making the decision to bring him home. It just made him try harder and harder to get her attention and to get her to love him, but it kept backfiring. His behaviors escalated to match her resistance. The more he tried, the more she reprimanded him for his uncontrolled love.

She spoke to him consistently and firmly to get him to stop walking on the furniture, although he still would do it every time she left the house because he wanted to prove to me that he was boss. To an extent his plan was working because he really upset her and it kept her off-balance.

If someone is clingy, there is usually a good reason somewhere that can be found in their past experiences. Funny, Kate's past experiences taught her to avoid clingy people. Yet here she was, stuck with clingy Joey. He never let her out of his sight. No matter what time of the day or night, his dark eyes would be watching her every move from beneath his shaggy brow. He pushed all her buttons and that's how she knew that he had something to teach her. If there's anyone we are sure to learn something from, it's the one who pushes our buttons.

She knew she was not being completely loving with him. She was especially upset that he had disrupted her relationship with me. After a few months she realized that things would never improve if she didn't change her ways. She knew that it was up to her to find a way to love him, so one night the three of us made some popcorn and we all sat together on the couch and watched the movie "Benji". Benji looked so much like Joey! Joey even had a lot of the same behaviors. Benji was homeless on his journey through a life of being unappreciated, lost and alone. Of course Kate was crying throughout the movie, as she is prone to do, but it reminded her that Joey had been homeless too and that he was doing the very best that he could in his new life with us.

The Key to Everything

The next phase of our new life with Joey was challenging at best. Joey went through a stage of eating pens, other things made of plastic and pencil erasers. How would we cure him?

First she hid the magic markers and the highlighters. She didn't know what else to do. When he couldn't find the pens and pencils, he started chewing lamp wires.

Just before she threw her hands up in despair, she took a new approach. She stopped being so strict with him and started helping him to feel more at home with us. It was really good because he had never felt truly accepted by her. I was so happy because I knew that positive reinforcement is always more effective than criticism and punishment.

We always give what we need and Joey always gave his love. So she started giving love back to him. She praised him for good behavior and, laying down some ground rules, she spoke firmly but kindly to him when he misbehaved. She reassured him and kept proving to him that she would come back when she left the house. She started making a fuss over him every time she returned home so he would know he had been missed and was valued.

She finally proved that she loved him and he finally believed her. Then he didn't have to act out anymore because he felt secure with her. This happens to people too. They need love and kindness to be at their best.

Not only was Joey more secure, but he was also on the road to a long and healthy life. Animals are a lot like humans for when we are happy our immunity is strong and love and life force races through our veins. When we are depressed our immunity runs low and we can easily get sick. Many pet parents are very careful about feeding the right food, providing plenty of exercise and buying the right toys and treats. Not that those things aren't important too, for they are, but the best thing you can do for us is to make yourself happy because when you are happy then we are happy too.

Mind Expansion

Someday, when you too arrive at Rainbow Bridge, you will find that you remember everything that ever happened during your time on earth. When they say your whole life passes through your memory, it's true.

Each of us has a vast computer with unlimited storage capacity planted deep within our DNA. It has nothing to do with the memory that comes from the thinking brain. It's the eternal memory and unlimited intelligence that is accessed through the heart. There are many things that happen, lifetime to lifetime, that contribute to our knowledge, our evolution as spiritual beings and our ability to love. Sometimes things happen in our lives and we never fully realize their impact until it all comes together later.

Long before she knew me, our Master was putting together a plan for her. There were important things she needed to do on earth and she needed the right people and pets to travel through life with her to help her accomplish her goals. I watched her from here. I watched it all unfold.

She had just ended a turbulent relationship, had a publishing deadline coming up and was in the middle of a career change. She decided to leave her busy life in

New York and reserved a house for a week in Sedona to do what she needed to do.

She finished the project for the publisher in just three days. She has always been the kind of person to get the least fun stuff over with so she could get to the rest. She took with her over 1400 pages of notes for a novel based on her relationship with Benito, a complex and highly spiritual Mexican immigrant who changed her life. He was a bit of a secretive man but he gave her glimpses now and again of his life story. Enough glimpses to intrigue her to write it. Not only was it a love story, it was an experience that opened her mind to life's possibilities. He taught her about spirituality and about the deep and pervasive connection that everything has with everything in the Universe. Our Master had attracted her to him for good reason.

Life is a hall of mirrors. Despite being 3000 miles away from her, Benito always seemed to know how she was feeling, what she was doing, even what she was wearing! One night her friends Lynette and Al invited her to go out for some drinks. They also invited Al's friend, Dan to come along. They went to a bar on the corner to listen to the band. She was missing Benito, so she ordered a bottle of Corona and lime, as if by doing so she would be closer to Mexico and closer to him.

The next day Benito called her and he asked her teasingly, "So where were you last night?"

18

"Why do you ask?"

"Because I saw you wearing that red sweater that I like. You were at the corner bar in the corner booth drinking beer with your friend and her boyfriend...and that other guy too."

She was awestruck. She did not yet understand how the intangible connections work between lovers. It would be the first of many things that would come to open her mind.

One night she was happily preparing for a trip to Mexico. Romantic Spanish music was playing on the stereo and she was sipping a glass of wine while she packed. She was so excited, for she was going to visit him after many months of separation. She was almost dancing around her room as she packed her suitcase full of her prettiest dresses.

Grady was there with her. It made Grady so happy to see her so happy! Grady left the room and came back with her favorite monkey toy and was wrestling around with it. Kate stopped packing long enough to play with Grady for a while. They danced around the room together, laughing. At one point Kate took Mr. Monkey by the arms and pretended to waltz with him. Grady barked excitedly for she wanted to waltz with him too! Grady followed Kate and the monkey over to the dressing table where Kate paused to look at a photo in a frame of Benito. While dancing with the monkey, she spoke to the face in the photo.

"Hey Benito... how is it that you can see me? Do you see me in your mind? Do you see me in your dreams? Maybe you see me through the eyes in your picture! Well Mr. Know-It-All, if you can see me now I wonder if you can see who I am dancing with!" Then she was off waltzing around the bedroom again with Grady and Mr. Monkey.

Benito called her the next day. He gave her his latest news. He couldn't wait to see her. When the conversation was almost over she asked him.

"Did you see me last night?"

"Yes," he said. "Yes I did!" and before she could say anything else he added, "but I couldn't see who you were dancing with!"

Now, when she looks at my photo, she thinks she is looking at me, but she knows that I am also looking at her. When she dreams of me she knows that I am dreaming of her too. People who can see things from other points of view can understand this better than most. We always go where we think your attention goes. We know you are looking into our eyes because that is where the power is, even in a photo.

The eyes are where the eternal fire of the soul resides. So the next time you look at a photo of your best friend, put yourself in their shoes and see how beautiful you are!

Destiny
Plays Itself Out

As she was researching and writing the novel, she would read Benito excerpts from it and he would say incredulously with his eyes wide, "Wow Katalina, how did you know that? That is exactly what happened!"

Or he would start to tell her a story and she would reach over and gently and mysteriously put two fingers over his lips, pull out her novel notes and read the same story back to him almost verbatim. It was amazing. It was about soul connection and the knowingness that comes when you allow things to naturally flow in your life.

Some souls come together just for a little while to teach each other something. It can be confusing because you can think you love someone at first sight and you assume that they are a soul mate. You think it's supposed to last forever. You share the same dreams because when your mind is asleep, your souls travel to the same place so that you can be together. You think of them and they call within moments, because they are thinking of you too. The truth is that some soul mates stay just long enough to teach you what you need to learn.

It can get a little complicated when you have the expectation that you're supposed to live Happily Ever After with this person when they were designed to stay with you for just a little while. Our Master designs it this way so you make the most of the relationship when you have it. She thought all soul mates were meant to be forever, when some soul mates are just meant to be.

Time Brings Change

Looking back, being appreciated is what made the difference between my living a life and my living a beautiful life. We are blessed when our loved ones know what they have long before they lose us.

It's the same with people. If they are taken for granted long enough, they can be oppressed to the point that they never experience the joys of life. Life on earth becomes a disappointment for them and Heaven becomes their goal. On the other hand, if they are loved and encouraged and appreciated, they will find all kinds of reasons to keep on living! It is never too late to help someone to see that they are valuable and wanted upon the earth.

When I was younger she thought she might outwit time. People would ask her how old I was and she would fib to them and tell them, "He's three," when I was five or "He's five," when I was eight.

They would reply, "Aw! He's still a pup!" and she'd smile because that's what she wanted to hear. She wanted to think she could turn back the clock and keep me longer than she could have otherwise, but when it's your time, it's your time and that's all there is to it.

Then there were the Sundays. I loved Sundays! She reserved Sundays just for us. First we'd all have breakfast with eggs and bacon. She was always so happy and relaxed. Then when we'd had our fill, we'd pile excitedly into the car and head on over to the park.

Group obedience classes took place there every Sunday at 3 p.m. We would hike the trail by the river and then we'd sit in the shade of our favorite mulberry tree. Sometimes we ate lunch under that tree. She would sit on a giant hump of root that came out of the bottom of the tree, kind of like a lounge chair. She would sit there and lean her back up against the hollow in its wide trunk and she and Grady and I would rest in its shade until class began. I don't know if the hollow was there for her or if she created the hollow with all of her leaning and her love. Either way, Grandfather Tree was her medicine. It always brought her comfort.

Obedience training teaches us on many levels. It ultimately prepares us to be obedient, but it's not all about training the dog. A lot of the training is focused on teaching our master how to set boundaries, to be consistent, to ask for what is wanted and needed and mostly how to keep the upper hand and help us to see that our master is the one in charge.

People would ask her, "How's the Obedience Training going?"

She'd reply laughing, "You know I'm beginning to think that every woman should take this kind of training before they get married."

We always lined up for class at three o'clock. Kate and me, we tended to hang out a lot with a pretty lady and her German shepherd named Thalia. I thought Thalia was the prettiest girl I'd ever seen. In our first class Kate wasn't paying attention and my leash got all tangled up with Thalia's. From that day on, she and the lady and Thalia and I always hung out in class together. I liked the lady a lot but I never knew her name. So often the humans will ask each other, 'what's your dog's name?' and never think to ask each other what their own names are. I always thought that was kind of funny.

I knew that time was passing because I watched Grandfather Tree get bigger and bigger. Some time into our classes Thalia and the lady stopped coming. It would be a long time before I would know what happened. I didn't worry about it though because I knew that there are always good reasons for everything and that one way or another we would all eventually see each other again.

Slip Sliding Away

The park was always such a magical place for us. We started going there when I was really little when we still had my sister Grady.

Once when I was a young pup, it was a chilly October day. I was investigating the edge of the manmade pond. It was very interesting! It also was green and slippery with algae on the edge and before I knew what was happening, yikes, I slid right in! I didn't know how to swim yet. I was on my leash and when she tried to pull me out, she slipped in too!

We were shivering when we finally got out of there and we were both glad that we had a big blanket in the trunk of our car to wrap ourselves in. Even though we were soaking wet and chilled to the bone, it was really fun being wrapped up in that blanket with her.

Grady just looked at us like we were nuts. I knew never to go too close to the pond again. In fact I never much liked going in the water after that. After all, sometimes when we are young enough we never quite get over being startled by something we didn't expect.

Tangled Leashes and Lives

It's so funny how our humans can get all tangled up in our leashes when we see other dogs along the way. You might think it's because the dogs are unruly or that the owners don't have full control of the leash, but in actuality it's the Universe conspiring to bring certain humans together.

When you get tangled up in a leash with someone else, it's how we let you know that you are supposed to know each other. Maybe they have a message for you from us. Maybe they are just someone you are supposed to know. Us dogs are doing our best to push our loved ones along the road to destiny. Pay attention to those with whom you are tangled for they may have something to teach you or a special gift to give to you. It isn't always apparent in the first meeting. Nothing usually is.

One day at the park we met an old guy named Dale who had two border collies, Mandy and Cricket. All of us dogs would run around together, playing as best we could, despite the restriction of our leashes. We would get all tangled up and sometimes tangle up Dale and Kate who just laughed it off and kept untangling themselves. We would see them frequently and we came to

27

love Dale and his girls. Then one day we didn't see them anymore.

A number of years later, we met a nice lady named Lois. She was a new neighbor at Wild Horse Mesa where we lived and we all became fast friends. We all looked out for each other.

One day Lois was showing Kate her photo albums and there was Dale! And the two border collies too! It turns out Dale was Lois's husband and those dogs were their dogs! Mandy had crossed Rainbow Bridge by then. Dale often took Cricket on the road with him and they were working most of the time. Once Lois knew that we all knew each other, she'd get us together and it was a fun time!

Life on earth is so fleeting. It is a speck of time in the hourglass. The time came when Grady was getting ready for her passage. Kate had called the vet and made the appointment for the inevitable.

When Lois heard about it she announced, "I'm going with you. You aren't going to do that alone."

"No, really I'm fine," Kate replied. "Grady and I have worked the world alone most of the time, so it's only fitting that I do this with her alone."

"Nonsense," said Lois, "I'm going to be there Monday morning and we're going over together." That was that.

When Monday morning arrived, Lois wasn't there. Kate thought it odd since Lois was the kind of person who would always do what she said she would do when she said she would do it.

You read in my first book what happened with Grady at the vets. It was so amazing and beautiful. Still, Kate was crying all the way home. She missed Grady so and, as most people do, had many complex emotions about putting her to sleep.

As Kate walked through our door the phone was ringing. It was our good friend and neighbor Freda.

"Oh Freda," Kate whined, "I've just come back from putting Grady to sleep."

"Oh I'm so sorry Kate, and I just learned about Dale."

"What do you mean? What about Dale?"

"Didn't Lois tell you? He died! At 4:30 this morning."

Kate was speechless. She began to feel guilty that she had been feeling so bad about Grady when here Lois had lost her beloved husband of thirty years.

"Oh dear, I've been swept away with grief over my dog and now Dale is gone too."

The fact is that Dale and Grady had made a pact long before they ever came into this earthly existence. This is why so often there is one physical death that follows another. They are from the same soul family. They are so intertwined that they need to leave together. They are all returning home together.

Seeing Thalia

When she took me to the vet that day for surgery, there was a man there waiting at the front desk looking very somber.

"Just a minute, Luke, Thalia's almost ready," said the vet tech.

Kate was focused on talking to the lady next to us, but I looked right up at the sound of Thalia's name. I was on alert, my tail wagging, excited that I might see my old girlfriend from class come around the corner.

The man was telling another man that Thalia had been on IV's all week. She had high levels of some kind of metal in her system. She wasn't expected to survive. The man was taking her home so that he could care for her in her final days. I felt bad because I knew how sad it was going to be for him.

They brought Thalia out in a wooly blanket and placed her in the man's arms. She looked really different, but it was definitely my friend Thalia. I would not have recognized her, but I smelled her and I also smelled the toxic bitter sickness that pervaded her system. It made me very sad to see her this way.

Her eyes met mine. *I'll see you soon, Jack,* she said to me.

Kate got up to open the door for them as they were leaving. "I'm so sorry," she said to the man. I don't think she realized that the black and silver dog draped in his arms was our friend Thalia. He nodded with appreciation but offered no words. She returned to the waiting room.

"I don't know why the guy wouldn't just put his dog down now," the lady next to her commented. "Why take it home to suffer?"

It's not putting us down. It's lifting us up.

"Maybe he has a lot to say to her," replied Kate. "Maybe he doesn't want to put her to sleep; maybe he is hoping she will cross the Bridge on her own terms."

"Humph. Maybe."

They had no way of knowing that Thalia and I would be crossing Rainbow Bridge together later that week on the very same day at the very same time. She and I were part of the same soul family. It was all by Design.

My Day of Departure

Joey stayed with Lois the week that I was sick. Early in the day of my passing, Lois brought him over to our house for a visit. Kate was nervous about it because she was extra protective of me in my condition. Joey was just so high-strung. Kate worried as I lay there helpless on the floor, but when Joey approached me long enough to say goodbye, I was really glad to see him. He was very well behaved for he understood what was happening. We needed that time together, him and me. It gave Joey the opportunity to say goodbye to me and it gave me the chance to say goodbye to Joey. Closure is very important, for your other pets and for your children too.

Later as my final moments on earth approached, things happened so fast and yet seemed to move in slow motion. When the time came, I would not close my eyes. I felt that if I closed my eyes I'd be giving up on her. Like little kids when they play the game Now You See Me Now You Don't. When you cover their eyes, they don't know you are there, even though you are there. I was afraid if I closed my eyes that she would disappear. My mind was already affected.

During the hours that I had been in and out of consciousness that night, the angels came to tell me what I could expect and how to get where I needed to go. I was reassured that I would not have to cross the Bridge alone. There were many things I did not yet know. I could feel my mental clarity leaving. I fixed my gaze upon her. I watched her as I left. It was like shutting the door of a beloved home for the last time. Like closing up camp for the season. One last look at the ocean before you must leave it behind with hopes of return but with no guarantee. You eventually have to turn away and look the other direction so that you can see where it is you are going.

I loved her. I did not know what state of mind I would be in when I got where I was going and I was most worried that in the process I might forget her. I did not ever want to forget her! I held the image of her in my mind so strongly and the eternal love for her so deep within my heart that it could never ever be erased, no matter what. My love for her was stronger than anything that could happen to me.

As I let go of my earthly body and my worries, everything was replaced with love. When we say we live on inside your heart, it is true. It was as if I was funneled down a tunnel deep inside my heart that expanded out into a whole big kaleidoscope world, larger than life...all inside myself.

I woke up right after I thought I had died. I woke up on our back steps at our house at Wild Horse Mesa. I was a little confused because the last thing she said to me was "Go Home little boy." I always did what she asked me to do. Our house at Wild Horse Mesa was the home we shared the longest, so it was my first thought. So that's where I went when she told me to go. For a split second I had forgotten that we had lost the house.

You probably haven't thought much about lizards being anything but lizards but I had a good friend named Lizard. He had been preparing me for this final earth journey for a very long time. He wanted me to be comfortable with every last detail. So when I woke up at the wrong house, I was a little nervous. Lizard was a soul mate of mine so when I got nervous he could feel it in his soul and he rushed from wherever he was right to the scene. He told me not to worry and he showed me how to get back on track.

He then congratulated me on having graduated into Heaven's realm. He told me how, in the blink of an eye, I could revise my itinerary and go right to where she is. But I can't go there yet. First I have to cross the Rainbow Bridge where I will eventually receive my wings and in the proper time I will be able to go wherever I want to go.

She still lived in the house we lived in when I left her. Because I loved her best of all I wanted to go there instead of to the

Bridge, but things were already different. I was 3 ½ years old again, aged 25 in people years. I would never get any older! Can you imagine? It all happened so fast. I just went to sleep in one place and woke up in another.

Over the Rainbow

In no time at all I was at the edge of the Bridge where they were all waiting patiently for me. It's hard to describe concepts that are not known upon the earth. There are not words to describe what is beyond description. I had been well prepared by my angels and guides so that I would know what to expect, but I couldn't really fathom it until it was actually happening to me.

The first one I saw there was my friend Thalia. I was so happy to see her and she was happy to see me too! She looked beautiful! We were meant to know each other and we would cross the Bridge together. I was glad I'd learned to get over my fear of crossing bridges when I took agility classes with Kate. It was good preparation for this journey.

Off we went, across the Rainbow Bridge! Have you ever had a dream where you ran like the wind? Or maybe you even flew? That was a glimpse of how your soul travels through the heavenly realm. You dream it because your soul is traveling there when you dream. When we lived on the earth, we saw everything in shades of grey and brown and white. The whole spectrum of color opened up to us as we crossed the Bridge of deep purple, scarlet, orange, green, blue and yellow. Everything was vibrant and alive. The colors themselves were alive.

They say love is a journey not a destination and it is true. Rainbow Bridge is a journey, not the destination. It is made of love and light and it is the direct pathway to Heaven.

Thalia ran along with me but every so often she would stop to look behind her. She was watching to see if her master might be following like he always had before. But he wasn't following her. I knew he would if he could.

Don't go back there, I told her. *Our true Master is on the other side. My Kate and your Luke will be coming here soon too. It's okay. We don't need to worry about anything.*

Even so, I found myself wanting to wait for Kate. I have to admit that I was looking back too, but I had been told that it's not good for someone to spend too much time on the Bridge, even though many do. The Bridge is the passageway but it can become a place of limbo if one spends too much time there, not able to move forward, not able to go back. Most of us have a hard time letting go of the life we lived on earth, even though the beauty of Heaven beckons us on from the other side.

For some the journey can be a difficult one because they feel they are tearing themselves away from someone they love on the earth. When the loved one also clings it can trap both of them in limbo, a type of tug of war, between Heaven and Earth. They have no rest until this is resolved. The one crossing the Bridge is caught in a series of cobwebs made of thought forms that block their freedom to cross. When those thoughts have cleared, the webs disappear and they are free to travel easily, the rest of the way Home.

I was already learning a lot from this rainbow journey about a lot of things. For example, I always knew that cats were funny, different than us dogs. Cats are unique and cats are very gifted. They are sage healers with deep insight, but they don't get hung up on the need to please. They get right to the point. Often when they get old enough, they just strut away with their tails in the air. Disappearing from life without much drama, they walk proudly all the way to the Rainbow. So all the cats, they were walking, leading the rest of us the rest of the way.

I kept nudging Thalia forward. Eventually we traveled over the Bridge together and as we approached the other side, Thalia stopped suddenly in her tracks. She surprised me when she let out a joyful whine before she then picked up her pace and moved steadily forward. Soon she was running faster and faster. Oh, she was running like the wind! She ran straight into the arms of a beautiful angel on the other side. That angel was her earth mother. The angel was the nice lady from the park! It was the lady that always joined Kate and me for class. Oh she looked beautiful too! The joy of their meeting was indescribable!

There was a big long welcoming line of those Thalia had loved from every life she had ever lived. The more lives we live, the greater our love grows and she always loved this woman the best. This is where she really wanted to be, at home with her best friend. Here they were, drawn back together by that great magnet of love. The strongest loves are the ones who greet us first.

As soon as Thalia didn't need me anymore, I found myself missing Kate a lot. I had not yet crossed all the way across the Bridge. I found myself looking back to see if she was there. I used to look back on our trail and she always had been there before. But no, she was not there. I could not see her but I could feel her. I could feel her grief. I could feel her love for me, like a magnet, pulling me back over the Bridge. Back the way I had already come.

Everything changed when I saw Grady. Boy was I happy to see her! She helped me to focus on going the rest of the way. It was a commitment I needed to make. When she shared with me how amazing it was in every way (and I knew it was true for the way she sparkled with life and love like I had never seen), I made the decision to move forward.

As I traveled further into the beautiful world beyond the world I thought I lived in, there was a huge waiting line waiting there for me too! Grady was just the beginning. I saw so many friends. Good friends! Friends I didn't even remember existed until now. The ones who loved me the most were the first in line. I missed Kate, but I knew it was not possible at this time to have her here with me.

It was a big welcome party, everyone back together again. We all remembered each other. Everyone is a friend in the heaven that is our Home. We are all soul mates. You cannot imagine this place, even in your wildest dreams.

So many people are afraid of the ending of their life on earth. Then there are others who are afraid of not being able to leave after their bodies have long failed them. There's nothing at all to be afraid of. Death is the last lesson in the school of life. It is the final stage of growth. Death is the one event that is designed to remove all of your remaining fears. Someday you will find that the things you were most afraid of, like death, were only illusions.

Death. I wish the word could be removed from the vocabulary and from the dictionary. It simply does not exist, except in the human mind that was taught that it does exist. People think they are a body and they come to believe that when the body dies, everything they are will die too. It's not true. The soul lives on. The soul of consciousness exists not only in the body but outside of the body too. We are all souls that cannot be contained or limited by time or space or the physical body. For souls there is no death.

—

Never Alone

As I was happily reuniting with Grady and some other friends, I heard someone calling my name. It was a commanding voice. "Jack!"

I raced back to the Bridge. I was so excited! I thought maybe they were calling to tell me that Kate was coming! But no, I was being summoned. They were recruiting me to go back to escort Kate's father across the Bridge. No one crosses alone without someone they know and love beside them. I was the chosen one.

When I crossed the Rainbow Bridge with Thalia in the wee hours of that morning, I would not have expected Kate's father to be crossing over the following afternoon. It was complex, for while she wept bitter tears for me, she also cried guilty tears for the fact that, while she loved her father a great deal, she simply had loved me more.

Dealing with yet another loss interrupted her grieving process with me. The anger stage she was supposed to go through with me she applied to her father instead. Once she was done dealing with her grief over losing him, she would have to come back and finish the grieving she started with me.

I was told why I had to leave the day before he did. It was because they needed to teach me what I needed to know to be ready to best assist him. Lizard was my role model. He had shown me what to do and I had been well prepared.

When I arrived back on the other side of the Bridge to collect him, it was very hard not to think about going to her instead but I promised them I would stay true to my mission. It was the hardest thing I ever did, to be that close to her and to walk away again. My Rainbow friends had promised me that they would teach me how to be with her despite the veil between us, so I focused on that and it gave me hope.

It's interesting that they chose me to be the one to escort him, but I guess it's because he had one more lesson to learn before he got to Heaven. When Chuck walked the earth, he was one of those people who didn't quite understand that I was a thinking feeling being just like him. He thought of me as Just A Dog, but then he would glare at me if I acted like one; if I barked or got too rambunctious or got my nose too close to his food.

I was so surprised by his reaction when I came back to get him that day. Boy, was he happy to see me! It's interesting how you learn how much someone loves you when they thought they were all alone and then you show up for them. I was there with him because the moment we leave this world our Master makes sure that we are not alone. Not ever.

I thought it was quite amusing how Chuck kept walking with a limp all the way across the Bridge, as if his knee still hurt him.

You don't have to limp anymore. You don't have a reason to limp anymore.

"I know," he replied, but his head hadn't yet caught up with the miracle that was happening. Sometimes the head takes awhile catching up with what the heart already knows. He was still stuck in the belief that he was who he was on earth, with his limitations in body and mind. His body was free and yet still he limped all the way across the Bridge, at which point he was sent to the Rainbow Healing Center to correct his thinking so that he could be free.

I knew she would be okay because when you keep yourself very busy with tasks, you don't have much time to grieve and feel sorry for yourself. She was getting ready to go into the city to close out her father's apartment. We would all be very busy in the days ahead.

She had cured me of my fear of bridges but nothing had been able to ease my apprehension over the unpredictable slam of the teeter-totter. After we returned to the other side of Rainbow Bridge, I went into the Healing Center too, to resolve that issue. We cannot take any fear into Heaven with us because love does not coexist with fear and

Heaven is all love. The only way to be free is to rid ourselves of the fear.

A Reason for Every Fear

Fear always starts somewhere. I always loved the thunder and lightning storms, mostly because she loved them. It's all I knew. I associated them with something that is welcomed.

I was a very young pup. She would hear the thunder rolling in the distance and as it got closer and closer she would perk up and say, "Wow Jack! Here it comes! Yay! The storm is coming! It's so exciting, the thunder and lightning." She made it like a game. It would come closer and closer and I would be excited too, by the time it arrived. No matter what we were doing, we would stop and sit and watch the thunder and lightning. She would say "Ooh and Ahh," like it was a laser show or something. I was just happy when she was happy, so thunder and lightning storms made me happy too.

We did the same things when the coyotes would howl. Lots of them would surround our property, sometimes on all sides and they would howl like crazy in the middle of the night. I would sit bolt upright in the bed, my mind on full alert, and she would say, "Ooh! Listen to those coyotes! Wow! They are having a good time!"

I was always amazed how the coyotes came out between dusk and dawn. They are mysterious animals, and magical. The animals that come in what we call the "Tween Times" (in-between times between night and day and day and night) typically are teachers and messengers. Like a crack in a shell, they slip through the slice of light on the either end of each day.

But poor Joey! He was always afraid of the coyotes. He would run to her; he'd cling to her. She would say to him, "There's nothing to be afraid of, Joey. They're out there and we're in here and it's okay," but no amount of reassurance could convince him.

When things happen early in life they can leave permanent scars on our being. There was a good reason he feared the coyotes and it was not the reason she thought. She assumed that during his days when he was lost in the desert he had to hide from predators at night. It was true. He did. He learned from the lizards that he chased there to find safe little havens within the cactus bushes or in small dark places where no one could see him and no one could reach him. She thought he was afraid of the coyotes themselves, but there was a greater reason for his fear.

The real reason would surprise her. The wailing of the coyotes reminded him of the wailing sirens that night, the sirens that took his first love away from him. Rescue sirens would forever trigger his loss and abandonment issues. He would cling even harder to her when the coyotes came calling.

In much the same way, he would cling to her when the thunderstorms came. If she were paying no attention to him, he'd run and hide way under the bed or behind the big chair as soon as the bolts of light hit the sky or the rolling thunder reached his ears. She'd then try to convince him that the storms were good but he would have no part of it.

"What's wrong you Silly Boy? Why are you so scared? Everything's okay."

But Joey wasn't silly at all. Something was triggering the fear in his heart. Our deepest fears are all based in history. When there is fear of this magnitude, there is always a reason.

She didn't know his history, but I did. He told me all about it. He had been loved. A lady had him from the time he was a pup. He looked at her in the same way he now looks at Kate. He trusted her. He loved her.

One day an ambulance came to the house with sirens blaring. The paramedics lifted the lady out of their house and into the cab and shut the door. Joey was right at their feet but in the chaos they didn't see him there, he was so small. They sped off to the hospital thirty miles away. Joey chased them down the street. He ran and ran his little heart out until he could run no more. Finally he had to stop. At a picnic area just off the highway, he curled up in a little ball and waited for her to come back for him. Many days passed but she never returned.

The fact is that Joey had survived many desperate days and nights during the monsoon season. He had been lost, trapped in the thunder and rainstorms that battered him in the expansive wilderness with no place to run for protection. So of course he would be afraid.

He would come to suffer abandonment issues and terrific separation anxiety, but he would also come to love and trust and be loyal to the one who brought him home.

If he's lucky she can help him to learn to make peace with the storms in this life. She came to teach him that not everyone you love goes away. He came to teach her also that not everyone you love goes away. There's the old reliable mirror at work again. You find yourself teaching the very things you need to learn.

Losing Your Mind

There's a big difference between the head and the heart. Fear lives in the head. Love lives in the heart. The head thinks it knows it all but the heart is always right.

She found all kinds of things to feel guilty about. Her mind had turned against her. She was her own worst enemy. Her mind, a relentless attacker, created all kinds of reasons for her to feel guilt and shame. The reasons made no common sense for, after all, I lacked for nothing when I lived with her. I wanted nothing but her love for me. It was heaven on earth and she had always given to me freely. There was absolutely nothing for her to feel guilty about.

Sometimes people feel they need to control everything, as if they could! Matters of life and death are out of your hands. The more you come to realize this, the harder you try to prove that you can control SOMETHING, anything. All you can really control is your response to what happens. You cannot control matters of life or death and because of this you are not accountable. You cannot be held liable for anything that you have no power over. Guilt, shame and blame make no sense when circumstances are beyond your control.

The thing is, life teaches humans to live in their heads and then the humans spend the rest of their lives unlearning what they were taught. Relearning how to live from the heart helps them to live in strength of love instead of in the desperation of fear.

The heart fears nothing. The love in your heart is stronger than anything that can happen. We see, we feel, we hear, we speak and we love. We teach those on earth and at Rainbow Bridge through the heart first. We never forget each other. While holding one another precious, we learn to live and love again and we become more than we ever were before as we are transformed by our love for one another.

Love is the most powerful force on earth. The end of fear is where love begins. Then nothing can overcome you.

Rainbow Orientation

"We are not dogs, cats, humans, horses, lizards anymore. We are VIBRATION." This is the first thing I learn as I step over the bridge to the other side.

When we return to Heaven, as we all do, it doesn't matter if we have two legs or four, we all return to Spirit. We only need bodies to live on and to experience the earth. We do not have two legs here; we do not have four. We do not have legs! We aren't running around looking like "Jack" and "Kate" and "Chuck", although we can change form anytime we want to. We are not animal or mammal, or man or woman. We are not black or white or red or yellow. We are all alike. We are purely the soul of spirit.

Like a snail sheds its shell or a caterpillar raises from its cocoon, we only need our bodies to experience life on earth to the fullest. Our physical bodies are just the costumes our spirits wear to fulfill the roles we played while we lived on earth's theatre stage. When we cross into Heaven, we become a part of everything, all of us together. We are each part of each other. Like Humpty Dumpty, it seems inconceivable, but we are put back together again. We are one.

Love is the highest vibration. Fear is the lowest vibration. Even those who kill and abuse only do so out of fear, even though they seem to be strong. Violence always comes from the fear of something. We are all here to raise our vibration and learn how to live our lives in love. The higher up the scale, the closer to Heaven. Fear is at the bottom, love is at the top. This can be translated into Hell and Heaven, but Hell does not exist except in the mind of someone who vibrates at a low vibration.

Then again, a select few indeed live Heaven on Earth because of the love they see in everything. You cannot see what you are not.

Entering Purrgatory

Purrgatory is a sacred healing center that is run by the cats. Cats are some of the best healers of all time. Of all of the animals, they vibrate at the highest level. This gives them a very high tolerance for pain and nonsense and this is why they purr, for purring is Vibration Itself and this is how they help to heal others. When they rub alongside you they are doing Reiki healing. They tend to raise the energy in the space they are living in. This role has gone back to ancient times.

Upon arrival on the other side, before we enter the gates of Heaven, we are each tested on our personal level of vibration. If all goes well from lifetime to lifetime, our vibration will continually increase. The highest score is 1000. Only divine guides and angels can score a perfect 1000. The rest of us are somewhere below that. There are special Healing Centers designed for the lower scores and then a finishing school for those who are approaching the perfection of 1000.

If you have any unfinished business in your heart, you must go to one of the Purrgatory Centers to cleanse and be cured from your attachment to fears and certain memories. It's not a place of punishment. It's just a place where all spirits with unresolved issues go to purge their negative thoughts and to heal their souls.

You cannot truly be free until you are unencumbered and you must be free to be able to fly. Once you are free you will earn your wings. It is the goal of every soul. Once you earn your wings you can pass through the gates of Heaven at which point you can also return to visit your loved ones upon the earth.

Until we learn what we need to learn to live fully in Heaven, we must ask our higher vibrational friends to visit you on our behalf. This is why you see cardinals and rainbows, hummingbirds and other mystical, highly energetic beings come into your life shortly after we cross the Bridge. We help each other out and send messages of love through those who have already been through the coursework and proven themselves to be stronger than any circumstance.

Timing is Everything

Lois kept Joey for most of the week following my passing. When it was time for Joey to return home after I had left for Rainbow Bridge, Kate was not sure she even wanted him back. It was not that she was uncaring. It was because she was so grief-stricken that she could not see anything clearly.

It's not that she didn't want Joey. It's that she only wanted me. In her confused mind, if she couldn't have me, she didn't want him either. She didn't want anything but me. You simply can't take care of someone else when you aren't able to take care of yourself.

There is a period of one to two earth years that humans are to refrain from making big decisions. It's because you don't always make the best decisions when you are grieving. Those who make decisions in haste often live to regret them.

You must move through the time of suffering, strengthening your faith and being willing to grow through the grief in order to be able to see things differently. As you grow, your blind faith will continue to open your eyes. You will see everything in a whole new light when you come out the other side of grief. Then you will be able to make very good decisions for yourself, better than ever, because of what you learned.

Love is the strongest force in the universe. I have taught you to love so that you will love again and so you will get stronger and stronger. It may be a week, it may be a year, or less or more. Don't try to judge it or plan it out. If you want another pet, the right one will come to you at the right time.

Ashes and Afghans

It was the first time she went to the park without me. She had just been to the vet to pick up my ashes. It was raining that day; pouring just like it poured the morning that I passed. I knew right where she would go. She would always go to Grandfather Tree when she was having a bad time or needed to sort things out in her head. She sat down under the mulberry, which was thick with big leaves, so thick that the rain rolled right off of them while she remained dry underneath. She thought of me, her mind playing like a cinematic movie, reviewing the fun times we had shared. Her thoughts began to crescendo as she remembered the suffering of our final hours together. I did not want her to go to those memories.

Suddenly a car pulled up into the parking lot behind her. She heard a door open and close. It made her stop sniffling a little bit but she was kind of upset because she really just wanted to be alone. Who in their right mind would be out in this rainstorm? A moment later she turned her head and her tear-filled eyes to watch as they walked by. It was a woman walking with her Afghan Hound under a big red umbrella. What kind of person comes out to the park and walks in the pouring rain, she asked herself again. And an Afghan Hound? Kate had never seen an Afghan Hound in these parts. None of it made sense and she wondered if she was dreaming, but she wasn't. I sent the rain. I sent the woman. I sent the Afghan Hound. I sent the red umbrella. Remember what I said about things that make no sense?

The lady and the hound left. The rain eventually let up. She did not want to go home to the empty house but she was at a loss for what to do. She had my ashes in the car. Joey was still at Lois's. Her mind searched for a place she could go to escape her sadness but she kept coming up empty.

I was glad when she made the decision to go pick up Joey and bring him back home.

The Illusion of Time

Her grief kept getting in the way of a lot of the goodness that was trying to come into her life. Like a big cloud, it shrouded everything in darkness. She forgot about her faith in God and the angels. Joey was there with her and he tried to help, but you can't help those who are beside themselves. Her cup was half empty, which surprised me because she is the kind of person who could always see the bright side of everything.

It was actually kind of fun how I stopped her clock at 3 a.m. that morning as I crossed over into Heaven. I had left for Rainbow Bridge at 3:00 AM on the dot. It was always a goal of mine, to help her to learn to live in the moment. The whole time I knew and loved her, I wanted to show her that time was just an illusion.

The ticking clock always seemed to dictate everything we did together.

"It's time to go to work."

"It's time for breakfast!"

"It's time to go home..."

"It's time for our walk!"

"It's time for bed."

"It's time to take your pill."

She had just begun to learn how to forget about time during our final week together. It was a week when nothing mattered to her but me. She was with my every breath, every look, every beat of my heart and hers. When you live in the moment you find that you love more than ever. That's because when you live in the moment you get very focused on what is right in front of you. You put your thoughts on the back burner and you allow your heart to lead the way. This is why those who have had sick pets, family members and friends feel that they love them even more than they ever did before when it comes time for them to pass.

She used to reassure me when she left the house by saying cheerfully, "I'll be back soon!" I could sense that she didn't really want to go; I knew she'd rather stay home with us. It made me sad, but I tried to be cheerful for her too. Sometimes it would be twenty minutes and sometimes it would be many hours. Time really meant nothing to me then and now I live in a world where time doesn't exist at all.

No one here worships time the way they do on earth. When I tell you I'll be back, you know I'll be back. That's all that matters. It doesn't matter how long it takes or when or where. When we love we are always destined to meet again and it all happens in the blink of an eye.

Life Goes On

Kate did not venture out. She accepted no invitations. She sought the safety and security of her private domain with her memories of me. When one is deep in grief, it takes a toll on self-confidence. She did not feel she would ever be capable of doing anything again. She did not think she could even go to the store to buy tea.

I passed on the first day of the month so it was quite easy for her to count the days. She was newly obsessed with the passage of time, as if each day took me further and further away from her. It was a painful illusion. If the days must do something, they will bring us closer to our appointed meeting, not further away. Every time 3:00 rolled around, she relived the final moments. One day a week or so into the grief, she noticed that the clock on the mantle had stopped. At first she was surprised. We often do this kind of thing on purpose because we want you to feel surprise. Curiosity. Whatever it takes to move you out of your grief into feeling something else for a while.

"How ironic," she said, "how everything died when he died. Even my clock." It was not ironic at all; it was all by Design. And I did not die!

Her energy was returning but instead of feeling better, she found herself feeling frustrated and restless. While she was gaining momentum, there was significant discomfort that came with it. There was something she must do. It seemed monumental.

She knew it was getting to be time to leave the house, but she did not want to leave the house. It was getting to be time to venture out to get a battery to start the clock ticking again. She also needed food and to get her mail, which had been piling up at the post office, not that she cared. Most people don't want to go out for a while because it takes a lot of energy to go out into the big world and those who grieve have very little energy.

Looking into the mirror she hardly recognized herself. Her puffy eyes, the clothes she wore that she had slept in, woke in, slept in day after day as she tried to generate the strength in herself to return to the workday world. Her strength eluded her. She could not rise to the ordinary call to life. Alas, she did not have much time. There is never enough time when one grieves. Grief leads you to believe that life will never be ordinary again, and it never really will be for it is made extraordinary as it is touched and transformed by our greatest loves and deepest losses.

Eventually she began to see the seemingly harsh reality that Life Goes On for everyone else in the world, even though she was still in so much pain and it seemed that life had ended for me. Life had not ended for me at all. Things are not always what they seem.

Facing My Fear

While she continued to work through her grief, I was taking more orientation courses in the Healing Center. We can't help our earthly loved ones to overcome their grief if we don't understand how grief works or know how life goes on beyond life.

My teachers taught me many things. They taught me what to expect from the grief that Kate was experiencing. They told me there were five stages that she would probably go through called Denial, Anger, Bargaining, Depression and finally Acceptance. They wanted me to be able to understand her in the days to come so that I would best be able to help her to heal and learn and grow. They told me that I would play a significant part in her healing and that when I was finished with my classes I would have everything I would need to coordinate messengers, angels, signs and to visit her anytime I wanted to.

Since there is no room for fear or limitation in Heaven I still had something to do. At the end of class we had to confess what fears still remained. I only had one fear. It was fear of the teeter-totter. I needed to resolve it before I could enter the gates of Heaven.

One day during recess from my courses when I was out exploring, I found a beautiful agility course! There were pink flowers all around the edges and the equipment was shining gold and silver. I ran the course. I jumped through the donut, raced perfectly across the dog walk, in through the tunnel and out the other side. Then. I stopped in front of the faded blue and yellow teeter-totter. It looked so out of place. I started to walk away but then I remembered my coursework. I had been told that the teeter-totter is the one fear that is keeping me out of the gates of Heaven.

I don't know where I found the courage, but I went back to the entrance and ran the course all over again. I was determined this time. Whoosh, through the donut, straight across the dog walk, I flew through the tunnel and never missed a beat. Up the one side of the teeter and all the way down the totter. This one didn't slam down like I thought it would. It was a very soft landing, as soft as a cloud, on the other side. It was wonderful and I made plans to come back and visit the course again soon.

On my way back to the Center, I encountered a man sitting alone alongside Cocoplum Lane. He was just outside of Heaven's gates preparing for entry and yet he was crying bitterly. I was surprised he was unhappy because even the campus around the Healing Center is a happy peaceful place. In fact, it is totally peaceful from the moment you set foot on Rainbow Bridge, so I didn't understand why he was sad in a place that gives no reason for tears.

He was crying, he said, because he had planned to come here and haunt those who had been so mean to him during his life on earth but he now realized it had all been a waste of his time and that his lack of forgiveness and wishes for revenge beyond the grave wasted most of his time on earth too.

When I returned to the Center, I found out that this was the final course in my curriculum. I had passed the Agility Trials. Then they asked me what I thought they should do to the man on CocoPlum. His fate was in my answer.

You might think that this man would be sent back because he had more to learn but the fact is he would not be sent back at all. Forgiveness was his final lesson and his tears were simply evidence of his realization of the truth that he had learned from all those who had mistreated him on the earth. They were his teachers. He thought they were dragging him down when in reality they were propelling him to higher places. The man was to enroll in the Center for a short time before entering through the gates of Heaven. When someone has had an exceptionally challenging or difficult earthly life, those challenges are often by design. Our Master will test those who are ready to expand. The struggles are designed to increase one's strength and to be a springboard into higher realms.

All is Love

If we cross over and had a particularly hard time on earth or have unresolved issues that we carried with us across the Bridge, we spend time in a special place to heal our souls. It is not a place of punishment for sin. It is a beautiful garden city where all the streets are named after flowers and plants.

It is a place of Love for all. Love is the most healing force in the universe and love heals any and all conditions in a cocoon of safety and care. Regardless of who you are or what you've done or haven't done, the healing light of love will surround you and heal you.

I learned my way around the town. I would race around the agility course every now and then as if to prove to myself that I was no longer afraid. I was no longer afraid.

One day I took a shortcut down a side street and there was Mulberry Street! I had not been there before. I remembered my friend the shade tree at our park. I wondered if there was another one here. I entered the garden and there he was. Grandfather Tree stood tall and thick and proud near the sandy trail that led to the river.

This is where I met a man who committed suicide and another who was a serial killer. They were all seeking healing under Grandfather Tree. All of a sudden my issue with the teeter-totter didn't seem much of an issue at all. I met many people who changed the way I look at everything. I learned that no matter what happened in their life on earth that when we reach Heaven, we are all the same.

We learn from the healing review of our lives and then many of us later return to earth so that we can help others who are going through the pain and hopelessness that motivate someone to kill or to take their own life. Some people are crusaders and will step in full force to help or teach someone these lessons. That's usually evidence that they too have suffered something similar in a previous lifetime.

Moving Forward

It was a big step when she finally opened the door, started the car and put it into gear. Compelled to go, she felt she had no choice. That's because I was there prodding her along. I was encouraging her because I knew it was an important step in her progress.

She was well aware that she was rising above her grief long enough to accomplish the basic task of leaving the house. It made her even sadder because she felt that she was leaving me there. She felt that she was leaving me behind when she put the car into gear and drove away from our house and her memories of me.

She could not leave me behind. It wasn't possible. I followed her everywhere she went while her tormenting thoughts continued to seek me out. I love her but didn't like those thoughts! I wanted it to be her love that searched for me, not her torment. It made it kind of hard to be around her because I only wanted her to be happy again. I knew in my heart it would just be a matter of time.

The numbness of her denial was lifting like the morning fog. Her resulting pain was inevitable and she knew it. She braced herself as she neared the places we used to go. The special spots that held memories of her and me together.

As she approached and entered the bank, the grocery store and the post office, she tried to make herself invisible. She was aware that it was quite possible that she would see someone she knew. She feared that they might ask her a question that could not be answered without tears. She was so afraid of her tears! She was also afraid that someone would ask her to do something, when she could barely take care of herself at this point in time. How would they understand?

"Oh," she thought, "Nobody ever loved like this!" When you lose someone you love deeply and truly, nobody ever has it as bad as you. Many did not understand this level of loss. Others did, but she did not believe that anyone really would or could. She lived in fear of someone saying to her, "Oh c'mon, it was just a dog."

Little did she know, she would have moved through this distressing stage much faster if only she'd have reached out to others or allowed them to reach out her. If only she had not been afraid of her own tears. Her tears were her friends, for with tears comes healing.

She was still thinking of me quite a lot. She talked to me constantly. Everywhere she went I was there. She called my name and watched the skies as if she expected me to run to her from there. She could find no real peace of mind but she had to go back to work to pay her bills and to start living life again. There seemed to her to be no way out of it.

Slowly she returned to the world at large. She really had no choice, for those who are living must go on living. Yet at the same time she felt that she did not want to progress. Not really. Still so attached and focused on me, she felt that if she continued to grieve it would keep me closer to her. While it's true that grief keeps us closer, it also binds us together and keeps us locked in the grief when it's time to move on and live life again.

Earning My Wings

During the time that she was venturing out into the world, I was preparing to take leave of the Healing Center. I was very proud because I was then granted my wings. I had earned them by resolving all of my remaining fear and concerns. I was congratulated and welcomed by a huge gathering of angels. The first angel I saw there was Thalia. Wow, she looked so beautiful!!! Her coat seemed to sparkle in fibers of white and silver light.

After having learned so much about soul mates in the Center, I had come to realize that Thalia was also one of my soul mates. That's why I loved her so. That's why I loved her at first sight. That's why we connected again in our earthly life. Soul mates come around and around again to teach each other all about love. Now it was her turn to lead me. She was the one who came to escort me through the gates of Heaven, the final leg of my journey.

I saw many spirit friends who I remembered from my lifetimes before. Lizard had gone back to assist others over the Bridge. My beloved earth mother Sarah from several lifetimes ago was the one to bring me my wings and there was my old friend Hawk, who would teach me how to fly.

Oh Heaven is such a joyous place! Everybody gets along and lives in the highest vibration of love. Those who live in this vibration are happy, creative, caring, and helpful. It's a very busy place because the angels fly hither and thither answering prayers that have risen up from earth. They have all the energy they need and more because where once they were made of cells and bones, they now are spirit made of love and faith. We all have everything we need.

Once we get to Heaven we know everything there is to know. We remember every life we've ever lived. We recall everyone we've ever loved. There is much to know here, but there is not too much to learn. That's why we have to do our learning before we get here.

* Anger *

The numbness and denial were behind her. It was progress but she didn't think it was. She was starting to feel all of her feelings. As the shock of grief began to wear off, the first feeling that arose was anger.

"It's just not fair!"

"He was only 8!" She thought she'd have me in her life until 12 or maybe 13. Maybe more. She thought that she loved me so much that love itself would keep me alive. The fact is, that it has, but not in the way she was thinking.

"But we ate the best food; we walked twice a day!" This is the stage when resentment and bitterness can rear their ugly heads.

"We always lived our life in love. We did everything right!"

"Maybe the veterinarian did something wrong!"

It's all by Design. The ordinary human mind has a natural tendency to go to the anger as a matter of course and seek out someone to blame, anyone.

It takes a lot of energy to grieve. Anger is the body's way to start energizing. The fire of anger is power and power makes you feel strong again. It isn't pleasant, but it feels so much better after feeling so weak and vulnerable and helpless for so long. I can no longer leave the room when she gets angry. I cannot comfort her like I always could before but I have learned that this too would pass and she would find her own way.

Alas, there was no one to hold liable for her loss. Her radar mind could not find a place to put the blame. It was just life. It was just death. Where to point the finger? There was nowhere to put her anger. There was no one to blame.

Why the need to feel guilt and place blame? Do you call me guilty too? Do you feel that I failed you because I had to leave? One of the most important things I came to teach you is that you are not in control. Humans think they can control everything, when it's Out of Their Hands.

She says that I left too soon, but I left at the perfect time for me. She felt she had been swindled out of the three, four, five or more years she had planned on sharing with me. The biggest disappointments in life come from having expectations that life will be a certain way and then finding out it isn't. She knew all along that she'd outlive me, for humans usually do, yet she was acting as if she thought I should live on earth with her forever.

"Why," she would spurt, "Why? Why did you have to leave me so soon?"

You seem to forget that the sun must set. You knew perfectly well that I would not be with you long enough. Still, you weep and

75

cry and ask God 'Why' as if it were some kind of surprise. Why? Because love changes everything. Love's the surprise.

Going With the Flow

We shared so many good times together. Once in awhile we would spend a weekend at a cabin down by the river where every so often someone in an inner tube would glide by and wave Hello! We might all chat for a moment as they floated by on the river's current. All too soon we would wave goodbye. My tail would be wagging as they arrived and it would still be wagging long after they had floated away.

It's kind of like life. We come and we go. It's a constant ebb and flow. Embrace the moment; embrace everyone who comes along and be willing to let go when it's time to say goodbye.

I was watching over her. Every day I hoped she would wake with joy in the morning. Still I would see her wallowing through her grief. It seemed to get worse before it got better.

She suffered from complicated grief because of one loss on top of the other. First she lost me and then it was the death of her father. A month later she lost our house. She had built her dream house and over the course of the years it became her nightmare. There is enough fodder there to fill another book. But all for good reason for all that she learned! The most important thing is that the land that she bought and eventually built her life upon is where she needed to be, to be in the right place at the right time to find me.

She had a host of medical issues that came up. She developed arrhythmia, insomnia and other things after I passed. She drank a lot of wine and ate a lot of ice cream. She wanted the world to just fade away, seeking only comfort and an escape from her seemingly cruel reality. She had learned so much about taking care of herself in recent years, but from within her grief she saw little reason to keep going without me. She felt that her heart had shattered. She would never be the same. She was like the Living Dead. She was starting to feel more pain because she was entering another phase of grief.

* Bargaining *

In her case, the bargaining stage primarily took place when I was still alive, right after my surgery when she did not yet know if I would survive.

She would say "Dear God, If you just let him live a few more years in good health, I'll____ "(fill in the blank).

"Oh Jack if you get through this I promise we'll take more walks and I won't leave you at home for so many hours a day." And so on.

Her pleas went unanswered and ultimately she was forced to deal with the reality of my passing. The bargaining persisted even though there were no negotiations left. She would rewind her memory back to try to "find" the tumor. It was as if she believed that if she could find in her mind the cause of it, she could change our destiny and bring me back like nothing had ever happened.

Another form of bargaining, which many people do, and she did too, is to replay the final painful moments over and over in her head as if by doing so she could eventually create a different outcome.

It is natural to replay in your mind the details. Deep in your heart you know what is true. Your mouth speaks the words, "My cat has died," but you still don't really want to believe it. You go over and over and over it in your mind. Your heart replays the scene for you for the express purpose of teaching you to accept what has happened. While your heart tries to "rewire" your mind to accept it, your mind keeps looking for a different answer. It doesn't like the truth. Like anything else, when you hear it enough, you finally accept that it is true.

The problem comes when you get stuck on the replays. One of the hardest things to do is to discipline your mind to stop replaying the final hours. You must tell those thoughts to stay outside or go away. Tell them, "You are not welcome here!" Eventually they will obey you and fade away.

Kate still had moments when her thoughts would go to our final hours together. Where once she would have been wracked with sobs and tears, she learned to master control over it. Kind of like a song that is playing on the radio, the first few notes would come and she would recognize that it was a song she did not really want to hear, so she changed the station to find a better song. If you change your thoughts to a better thought, it will become a habit and the healing of your grief is guaranteed once you know how to do this.

Decisions

It was the dawn of a new day. Every day is like the first day of a new life. You can create whatever you want it to be because yesterday no longer exists.

She was starting to feel some energy and courage sprinkled between her anger and guilt feelings. She reached out for support to the one person she had always loved best. She reached out to the man she had been dating for the better part of a decade.

"I've never had a dog that died before," he said, "so I don't know what to say to you." She remembered that he had not been too compassionate when Grady passed many years before. He had not been particularly sympathetic about her father either.

She kept waiting for signs of support. Understanding. Attention. It took losing me for her to look at him and finally realize that it would never happen. She was looking for something he could not give. Even this is one of the gifts I gave to her, the gift of being able to see such things clearly. Grady had tried to give her this message when she left, but Kate could not see because her love for the man was blind.

Not everyone understands the love that takes place between two soul mates. Like lightning, once it strikes, you are never the same. As her soul mate I was the lightning that transformed her heart and taught her to love from the depths of her soul. You cannot experience this level of relationship with someone who has never had his or her soul touched by true love. You cannot fault them. They are on their own path. Don't be looking to them for more than they can give for you will be gravely disappointed and then resentful because they are not giving you what you think you need from them. If you do anything, pity them for not yet having learned what true love is.

I knew there was another plan and another man for her. She had spent a decade trying to make this man her man. Through this experience, she finally understood that she was not the one who could make things happen. Our Master and his angels are the ones who do. I was glad she was coming to terms with it because I knew she'd have a better chance at something much better coming into the space in her life if she would just let go of him.

She was also coming to realize that not every relationship is designed to be reciprocal. She had given many gifts to him over the years with next to nothing coming back. I could tell her all about what happened when she lived with him in a previous life, when he gave and gave to her with next to nothing coming back. Much like Benito who was a soul mate too, it was his turn to receive this time around. He had a good heart and she was God's gift to him. She was sent to him to bless him with her giving. He was God's gift to her to help her to grow in her insight and to learn to accept that there are certain things one cannot change no matter how much one loves or how hard one works to change them.

Late one afternoon on the man's birthday, she gave him a final gift. She went over to the special place near the creek bed on our trail and in her mind and heart she cut the cord from the man and released him from her unrealistic expectations. Like those on the river inner tubes, she let it pass.

Life can seem a series of purges. Sometimes when you think you have nothing left to lose it makes it easier to let go of the things that no longer serve you. One must be careful, however, not to make important decisions in the early months of grief— especially during the anger stage-- but in this case it was okay because the relationship was doomed anyway. She had learned what he had come to teach her.

I was concerned early on when she was thinking she didn't want Joey anymore after my passing. It would have been the wrong decision to let him go. But then, as a soul mate, she wouldn't have been able to get rid of him if she had tried.

DNA and The Big Bang

My buddy Einstein said that we only use at most 8% of our brain's capacity. I know this because one of my favorite things to do each night was to get into bed with her and learn from the books she was reading. She would read out loud to me the facts and then look at me and ask me what I thought.

"What do you think is going on with the other 92%, Jack?"

A cell has a nucleus and some other parts like membranes, plasmas and other stuff. Its energy is made up of protons, neurons and electrons. Genetic scientists, however, have discovered that the majority of a cell is made up of something unknown. Something akin to space filled with electromagnetic fibers of light. The human body is made up of some 37 trillion cells. What do you think you are made of? Who do you think you are?

It's all about God. You think it's me that you love, but it's really the God in me that you see. It's the God in me that you love. It's true. It's why we love you too. It's the God in you that looks at me and the God in me that looks back at you. It's just the Big Bang God in love with Himself.

"With my limited understanding what I think happened was that God decided to play a fun game. He created a great experiment and BANG and Kapoof! He exploded into millions of trillions of little pieces and they are each one of them us, scattered all over the universe. This would mean that we are all pieces of each other. We all belong to each other. I am part of you, you are part of me, always have been, always will be. If you put us all together, well, maybe that is God." (Jack McAfghan: Book 1, Chapter 40)

* Depression *

Sooner or later you realize that there is no bargaining your way out of reality. There is usually no one to hold responsible. You realize that it's just life and love and death. You learn that there is nothing you can do about any of it.

When I was a little pup, still at the Puppy Mill, Kate came to see me the first time. They told her that I was unruly and while she was there, they brought out a little Aussie Shepherd mix that was only four weeks old. They were trying to sell her too. I went over to sniff the pup and invite it to play but the puppy mill lady grabbed me and pressed me, my back to sidewalk beneath me. The puppy mill lady glared at Kate; she was angry with me. "You need to show these dogs who is boss!" She pressed me harder and harder into the sidewalk with her hands on my front legs like handcuffs. I could not escape. I tried for a little while but then I gave up because she was stronger than I was.

This is kind of how it is with grief and loss. You enter innocently into a situation. The situation challenges all that you have ever been. You fight, you flail, you do whatever you can to change it – to bring your loved one back – but all to no avail. You eventually realize that it is just a waste of your time and energy and you give up. You surrender to the circumstances. Like me pinned on my back to the sidewalk, it wasn't until I stopped struggling and became obedient that I was allowed to rise up out of the situation.

She could find no answers. She was hitting bottom. It's when you finally hit bottom, pinned to the ground by circumstance that you cannot control, that you realize you have to change and adapt. You realize that it's all up to you because there is no one else to blame and, if you are to continue living a sane life, you need to accept this fact and move forward. No one else can do it for you.

Again, it can get complicated. The fact is that when you admit that you can't blame anyone or anything else, you begin to blame yourself. The human mind gives up trying to find an executioner, but still it must blame someone. Anger that is not expressed tends to turn inward and, instead, attacks the very one who feels it. You move from anger and guilt into depression.

She became weak. The life force energy was not reaching her. She was oppressed by circumstance and if she had only gone inside her heart instead of her head, she would have found the strength instead of the weakness that came from her own masochistic thoughts.

"Why," she cried, "Why did you have to go? I want to be there with you!" So many people ask this of us.

If someone you have loved has crossed the Bridge and you are longing to be with them, I must tell you this: You must live out your life on earth and learn the lessons you are required to learn before you can cross the Rainbow Bridge too. You must grow from your life and your love and your loss. It's one of the things that we come here to teach you. To survive and to prove that love lasts forever.

If you leave prematurely, you will delay everything. It's like catching a train at the station. You need to be at the station at the right time and board the right train to get you where you want to go. If you leave earlier than you are supposed to, you can catch the wrong train and it will be very hard to get you back on track.

She was learning this. She was not quite out of the dark yet, but she was getting there. Everyone does eventually. She was moving towards acceptance. It was just a matter of time.

She would tell people, "He was my everything," but really she was my everything. She had her family. Her friends. She had her work. She had her writing. She had Facebook. She had things she had to do. What did I have? I only had her. So who is whose everything? This is why our Master designed us to leave first. We have to leave you first because if you leave us first, we don't have anything left. It's supposed to be this way. We need to cross the Bridge before you do so we can greet you when you get here. We wait at home for you there; we wait at home for you here. It's just the way it is.

Learning Choreography

It is one of those rare afternoons; she is out with her friends from work. They talked her into it. They are celebrating some kind of holiday. I am walking along with them, looking at things from her perspective. I listen to her heart, which tells me she does not really want to be there. She just went along because someone encouraged her to go and she knew she had to get out of the house.

She laughed with them and told them funny stories. She drank a beer and then a glass of ice water. She would often look off in the distance, her eyes not really focusing on anything. She thought about us all the time but she didn't talk about us much because her friends were kind of tired of hearing about her dogs all the time.

She thought of me. She thought of Joey, for while she was at the bar, he was home alone. She felt really bad about that and couldn't shake the guilt.

Poor Joey. After I left, he suffered terrible separation anxiety. She never knew he had this problem because I had always been there. I was always there to take care of him. We always learn so much about ourselves when someone we love is no longer there.

Suddenly in a rare and spontaneous moment when she wasn't thinking about anything in particular, I saw my opportunity. Earlier I had seen a man with clear blue eyes watching her. His eyes had a bit of a faraway look too. I will call him 'Salt and Pepper,' because I don't know his name, but that was the color of his hair. I liked him. I remembered him. He was the guy who had come to pick up Thalia from the vet that day.

I'd had him in mind for quite awhile, but he wasn't ready, nor was she. From the very first time I saw him, he fascinated me in a similar way that she fascinated me. I knew in a heartbeat that he would be good for her and her for him. The chemistry was right.

He too was venturing out into the world again, overcoming his grief just as she was. Here he was now, across the room, talking with his blonde friend. Oh how I wanted her to meet him! I imagined in my mind how I would do it if I had magical creative powers. Then I remembered that I did have powers!

"Hey, Luke!" someone called out from the far end of the bar.

She glanced up as the shout interrupted her thoughts. First she looked at the blonde guy at the far side of the bar and her eyes then traveled over to the man with salt and pepper hair who stood just beyond him. They rested on him for a moment with brief interest.

"Where do I know him from?" she asked herself.

It's Salt And Pepper Man.

She glanced over at Salt And Pepper a few times. She was drawn to him, but he and his blonde friend were surrounded by a group of pretty women. Seeing a flash of gold on his left ring finger, she looked away. Dang! If only he had taken his wedding band off! This was not going to be easy! But the best things sometimes take the longest to unfold.

It was not long after that she excused herself to go home. It was taking too much of her energy to be out in this social world. She was still depressed and grieving.

As she reached the privacy of her car, she got behind the wheel and began to cry. She drove out of the city and merged onto the interstate, brushing her tears away.

"How am I ever going to live my life? What kind of life is this, this limbo? I miss you so much. Jack, where are you? Whatever am I going to do?"

I am right beside you. Wipe your tears and see the beauty that is all around you.

"Just help me get home," she whined, to no one in particular. I detected a tinge of anger and frustration in her voice and it was good. It was the edge of her strength showing itself.

She exited the highway and drove down the two-way four-lane street out to the suburbs. As she slowly approached a red light, her tears stopped flowing and she watched, fascinated. Flitting and fluttering along the nearby sidewalk was a yellow swallowtail butterfly. It headed towards the busy street. She was concerned that it would fly into traffic and get hit, but it headed confidently across all four lanes. It skimmed happily across her windshield and into the second lane. It continued to fly across the oncoming traffic in the third lane and landed safely on the other side of the fourth lane. Many never saw it. Those who did, they did not know it was anything but a yellow butterfly at the stoplight.

What it was, was a messenger for her. It told her to STOP. Crying! Grieving! The butterfly represented the freedom that comes with transformation. The very action of a butterfly emerging from a cocoon is what builds its strength, its muscles and its ability to immigrate hundreds of miles or more. This inner power allows it to fly and rise above anything that is less than love. The power that comes from climbing out of a dark cocoon that binds.

It's bright, light movement was telling her that no matter how dismal things might happen to appear at the moment, she needed to rise above, to take herself lightly and to keep on moving forward. The light would turn green. She had to keep the joy in her heart and the desire to live. If we take ourselves lightly enough, we can rise above everything and arrive where we need to be, safe and sound.

Messengers often come when you struggle with a decision, need support or are trying to find your balance. They can come as animals like coyote and lizard appeared for Kate and for me. They can be spirit guides, angels, family members, ancestors and friends. A messenger can even be me! Many of them you will not notice because you are too preoccupied to see them. There may come a time, however, when you might sense the millions of angels too small to be witnessed, like fairies that live in the curve of a leaf or who sleep under the tiniest rose petal. I am glad she saw me in the flight of the butterfly.

We send signs to you to help you to grow, to encourage you to learn and to develop the faith that you are never ever alone and that the world beyond the world that you can see contains wonders you have not even dreamed of.

At the very end of our Classes we were taught some fun new skills. We were taught how to shape shift. We learned that we could transform ourselves into whatever we want to be. Between soul mates love knows no bounds. The abilities of the soul are unlimited. We can travel simply by thinking about where we want to go. Two souls together, no matter which side of the veil they are on, can communicate on a higher deeper level to meet at a specific time and place, like in dreams. We can send the hummingbird or we can be the hummingbird. We send the butterfly, the cardinal and the shooting star. Clouds are the easiest. Sometimes a bunch of us will get together and make a rainbow.

Releasing the Leash of Attachment

I was never on a leash on the wilderness trails and I never strayed far from her. Never let her out of my sight, in fact. I never walked ahead of her without stopping to look back to be sure she was still there. It's the same way now. I'm still here and she's still there.

One balmy night she was walking the trail with Joey. She was missing me. It was as if there was a big empty hole walking right alongside them where I used to be. She couldn't see how beautiful the evening was, but while she had tears and sadness, I saw that she was making progress.

"I know you're here somewhere, Jack. I don't know how I know it, but I do."

Little by little she had come to realize that I would always be beside her to love and protect her. Even though she couldn't see me, she could sense that most always and everywhere I was still there. The key was for her to connect with me in a balanced and unattached way.

From the very first night without me, she would light a candle. She didn't see that this was yet another attachment, another routine that she would one day have to break free from. After all, she would have to light a candle every night for the rest of her life. If she happened to miss one night, it would fill her with guilt for not lighting the candle for me that night. Losing an attachment like this becomes yet another loss to get over. The attachment is when you think your life or mine depends on lighting that candle every night for me. If your life is not complete without the shrine you made for me then you still have me on that leash around my neck.

Another lonely night, she was crying in the candlelight over a box full of mementos. My collar, sympathy cards, photos...with her broken heart she saw only a bunch of broken dreams. She looked at her life and saw no love there. It was like all the love in her life left the day I left. I want to come up with ways for her to know that she is loved, so I am making a plan.

We are never apart. We affect each other all the time by our state of mind. I made a pact that I would keep encouraging her until she was happy again. It would not be easy, for her grief was deep, but my Master tells me that everything is possible. Joy is our inherent nature. I always could make her happy before. If it's our nature, I don't know why I can't make her happy again. My Master seems to have faith in me; He knows that I can help Him to bring the joy back into her life.

Separation Anxiety

After I crossed Rainbow Bridge, things got a lot worse for Joey. He didn't adapt well to the changes in our lives. He missed me a lot. He became desperately anxious and more needy than ever. Kate thought it was all because I had left them, but it was mostly because Joey was so tuned into her and so sensitive to her changing moods that he was also picking up on her sadness and her desperation.

He became clingier than ever before which aggravated her because when someone needs attention they don't need someone else to need them all the time. The worst was when she had to go to work. Alone in the house for the first time in his life, his separation anxiety kicked in. She tried all methods to help him feel more secure. She gave him chamomile treats and talked to him and tried to soothe his fears. Reiki helped quite a bit, until the moment she removed her hands and he would go ballistic. When she was gone, he busted out of metal crates and tore up door jams and howled his fool head off so that she could almost hear his mournful wails all the way across town. There was no substitute for me and there was no substitute for her. So she gave up and just took him with her everywhere she went.

Little did she know another plan of mine was taking shape. Two seasons had passed since my departure. The hot Arizona summer would be upon them soon and she would not be able to take Joey everywhere because she would not be able to leave him in the hot car for such long periods of time. She also could not leave him home alone. She realized she would have to get another dog to be a companion for him. It was the only solution.

She felt she loved me more than life itself and yet as time passed Joey and I worked together to teach her that life goes on. She would come to teach him about true love by showing him unconditional love and he would teach her unconditional love by also showing her a love without limits.

Six Months

For the longest time she had searched and searched for me. Sometimes she would get desperate because she could not see me. She couldn't see me because she was looking for happiness outside of herself. I was living in the home of her heart while she was looking at everything outside of herself. It would be like her trying to find me out in the yard when I am inside the house waiting for her. Come in and close the door on the world and I will come to you, because I can.

It took the better part of six months for her to get a grip on herself in her life without me. For a long time I sent messages to her when she was grieving and when she was crying. She would not listen. She could not see. She could not hear. She had so much outpouring of sorrow and emotion that it was impossible for her to receive anything from me. It was like me trying to climb a waterfall to get to her. But if she could be calm and have faith in me, I could sail right over to her on the still waters of her soul.

Sometimes I would be right there in front of her and she would be looking the other way for what she thought she might see of me. I simply kept trying. I knew sooner or later that I would get through to her. Love always finds a way.

If it weren't for the dreams, I don't know how long it would have taken to connect with her. I used dreams to contact her because I knew that she always paid attention to her dreams. She learned what she needed to do to dream of me. First she would ask me to come to her in her dreams. Then she would get in a comfy position and place her hands upon her heart. She would then breathe deeply, focusing on the weight of her hands and the love in her heart and she would always find the calmness in her soul this way. Just in case I didn't hear her the first time (which I did) she would again ask me to come to her. It's important to ask for what you want from us because we always want to give you what you want even though, sometimes, we give you what you need instead. She would ask the angels to help her to remember her dream. Then she would close her eyes and go to sleep with her hands still on her heart ...and she would dream of me.

When you dream you go inside yourself – even though it makes you feel like you are traveling many miles and light years to go to the dream worlds. This is the irony of all of it. Everything lives within the heart of the dreamer. Your heart can take you everywhere. It's the world where we are still together. The heart is where you'll find me and anyone else you have ever loved with all your heart and all your soul.

The Dream That Set Us Free

If you've read our first book, you know about the dream that set us both free. For the longest time I couldn't come back, I couldn't move forward. I was in limbo because she was clinging to me. This is also why I had to go into the Healing Center. We have to put space between us in order to heal the pain when we are not capable of separating ourselves from it. When you become more evolved and aware, you can love just as much but not be so attached that you are immobilized by the fear that can come with attachment.

It was such a good dream; I'll share it with you now.

"There we were. I was in the corral looking up at her, standing high on the hill above me. As she started making her way down to me, I waited at the fence like always, calmly wagging and smiling. As she approached I turned and ran to the other side and waited there for her to open the gate for me.

She was dreaming, but she knew she was, and in her dream she knew what this meant. It was time _for_ me to be free. She wanted me to be happy and she knew she had to open the gate sooner or later. She was the only one who could do it. Now seemed as good a time as any.

She gently took off my collar. I sniffed it for the last time; smelling the lingering traces of my life on earth with her. She opened wide the gate and I ran out into the beautiful field of green grass and yellow flowers, blue skies and sunny day. I ran and ran and ran around, oh I was so happy! I was so free!

Then I stopped and looked back at her like I always did; to be sure she was still there or now perhaps to let her know that, no matter what, I still love her best of all.

I romped across the great field to see her one more time before disappearing into the forest. For just a moment I returned to the trees that lined the edge of the meadow for one more glimpse of her. I showed her that I was happy. I told her that I loved her. Then I turned and ran joyfully back into the woods. She waited there until she knew I wouldn't reappear.

Things always come full circle. I waited for her at the puppy mill gate when first we met. I waited until she was ready to free me from that life and become my earthly master. In much the same way I've been waiting again. I've been waiting for her to set me free to be with my Master here.

Upon waking from our dream she cried like she did the night I died. To her I died all over again, but I was reborn too. Finally she'd cut the cord that bound Heaven to Earth and by doing so she set us free.

Now I speak the words to her that she so often said to me when she went where dogs were not allowed:

I love you. You stay there. You can't come in. They don't allow you here. Everything will be okay. Wait for me. I'll come back for you. I promise.

And one day, in time that will pass in the blink of an eye, I will meet her at the gate and we will run together through the soft green meadow into a beautiful new world." *(Jack McAfghan: Book 1, Chapter 90)*

It worked! The moment she opened wide that gate changed everything for me. I was finally able to return to her in all kinds of fun and interesting ways. After all you can't return from a place you have not yet arrived, can you?

The very next day she scattered my ashes to the wind. "Fly free Little Boy, Fly Free," she said, as the remains of my physical existence were carried away from her on the gentle breeze.

It had gone on for six months her crying, searching, grieving, despite a series of unseen signs and miracles. It took quite a long time but finally I was able to come to her in a way that she could hear me. She started writing our book and then everything changed for both of us.

* Acceptance *

It was the first anniversary of my crossing. Late that afternoon she went out in the rain. She didn't really know why she went out there, but I think she heard my heart calling out to hers.

She went right to the place where we would sit after a long hike and overlook the creek bed below. If you've read our book, it's the place where I sent her the lightning bolt and the hummingbird moth. Today as she sat there she was talking with me, tears rolling, but her tears were different this time. They had more love in them and less sadness.

I covered her with my "signature" goose bumps. It was as close as I could get to being able to hug her from behind. It is always the same. That's how she knows it's me. The rain chilled her but her back was warm with my love. The contrast was dramatic. She knew who it was. She hugged herself in an effort to hug me too.

"Thank you Jack. Thank you. I love you."

Goose bumps are the tangible evidence of vibrational presence. If you have goose bumps, you know that it must be true.

Goose bumps are like Truth Detector Machines.

She was so pleased that I was there but then all of a sudden she started thinking about how much she missed my furry head and my golden brown eyes. She was missing my physical presence and was no longer satisfied with mere goose bumps. Tears stung her eyes and when they did it shifted her vibration from joy to sadness and I couldn't help it. I faded away and had to wait until she was calm again.

When the goose bumps went away, she was startled. She realized that they had been there and then they weren't...and when she put two and two together, she knew that it was her state of mind that had interrupted them.

This would be the turning point for her learning to connect with me. She needed to stay in her love and her joy. Her vibration needed to be a match to mine. When she could stay there in the love, we could be together. As she came to realize this, lo and behold, the goose bumps came back and enveloped her all over again! Oh I was so proud that she was learning what it takes to be happy.

One of the coolest things that happened was the night she missed lighting the candle for me. I knew that she would, sooner or later. She realized this and as I predicted, she had such incredible and silly guilt over it. She didn't know how happy this made me. I was rejoicing that she did not again need to celebrate the day that I had "died"! I only wanted her to celebrate my life and to know that we were only getting closer to each other as she was leaving her grief behind.

It meant that she had released me a little bit from the leash of her grief — that she did not associate me only with my death anymore. At least for that night! There would be more nights ahead. We look for signs and lights in the tunnel too, and this was one for me.

We used to joyfully experience my earth birthday. She would prepare a fun party celebration for me with all my favorite things. Now I celebrate my heavenly birthday. While I celebrate here, she still would mourn my death date there. She mourned each and every month, on my day of passage. "He's been gone one month, two months, ten months one week five days and twenty two hours..." Oh, if she could only see that it was not my death at all but the beginning of a whole new beautiful life. In fact, when we are re-born here, we don't come out crying like we did on earth. We come in laughing.

She would soon be finding the joy in life again. She would find the joy that had eluded her all this time because she thought that I was her joy. I can't say it enough times: When she is happy, I am happy too.

Staying Open

The phone was ringing. 10 p.m. She was worried that something had happened to someone for it was too late at night for the typical caller.

It wasn't a typical caller. It was her friend Barbara.

"Get out of bed and get down here!" she said, "There's someone you need to meet."

Barbara was calling from the local bar and grill. The two friends had not been out together since Barbara was married and since Kate had been sick. It had been over five years. It was time. She didn't go. I wish she had, but she just wasn't ready.

The next day Barbara stopped by Kate's house unannounced. Kate put a pot of coffee on and the two sat down at the kitchen table. Joey was climbing all over Barbara. He was so self-centered that everyone who came to the house he felt were coming to see him and he always wanted to give them a "proper" welcome. I think he learned that from me.

"Joey, get off!" Kate said sharply, as a good trainer would.

"Oh he's okay, leave him alone," was Barbara's reply.

Barbara was a bit on the bossy side and she thrived in a motherly role to her single girlfriends who she felt ought to be married by now. She was constantly trying to make things happen, while neglecting her own life and family. Some people try to correct the lives of others in an attempt to try to make up for the mistakes they have made in their own lives. Nonetheless, Barbara was Kate's reality check. She was my messenger. She was planting seeds of desire for love.

"Kate. You've got to move on with your life," Barbara was saying. "How on earth are you ever going to find your Knight in Shining Armor if you never leave the house?"

"I don't need to be rescued by a knight in armor because you can't get close to someone who wears a suit of armor all the time."

"Well," Barbara said pointedly, "maybe you are out to attract the ones who wear the armor so you don't have to take a chance on being too close to them."

Kate laughed uncomfortably.

"I'd actually just like to find a midpoint, Barb. I'd rather have a smart down-to-earth guy in a Carhartt jacket than a knight on a white horse."

Aha a clue for me. A Carhartt jacket.

Robert

Kate was getting pretty good at going out of the house. She went over to the local Farmer's Market one day. She went to get strawberries, potatoes and tomatoes but this time she also found a guy there. His name was Robert. She never planned to meet anyone interesting that day. It seemed an innocent and unsuspecting place. It was a very natural meeting and she was surprised they had such a level of comfort with each other.

They went out on a few dates and she liked him a lot, maybe even thought she loved him. I had taught her to love more than ever and she wasn't yet used to the level of love she was feeling that had grown in her heart because of me. She was already thinking that he might be "the one."

Sometimes when love comes on that strong, it's not always a soul mate. It's that you are so much in love with the idea of love that when you think you are ready, you fall in love with the first person you see.

A few weeks into the relationship, the phone rang. She answered, "Hello?"

"Yes hello," said the woman on the other end in a flat, formal voice.

"Who is this?"

"Do you know Robert Barnard?"

"Who is this?" Kate repeated.

"This is his wife."

Well, that was the end of that. We like to keep you in touch with the love in your heart and help you to believe in the hope of the love of a lifetime, while constantly nipping the things that aren't right for you in the bud.

It was nothing new. She would say, "Jack was the love of my life. There's nothing else for me." She was still grieving. This was her depression speaking. This is where she was stuck. You can't compare apples to oranges. You can't compare the unconditional love of a pet with the undeveloped love between two human beings.

Our Master knows you need love. He put the desire for it in your heart. He wants you to have a love that lives through every possible circumstance. He created animals to become pets to serve this purpose. He created human soul mates to serve this purpose too.

Human love is very different. Imperfect. Animals already know what they need to know. They know that they come to love and teach love. They fill a heart with love where there was no love before. Meanwhile humans seek perfect love all their lives while loving with an imperfect love. The results can be disappointing if not disastrous, but if two are willing to work at it and stay focused on the love, the results can be wonderful.

Back at the Trail

She was back at our special place at the foot of our trail. Robert was history and she came back around to thinking about me

She thanked me for all I had done for her and for helping everyone who reads my story. It has pleased me so much to help so many people.

I sent a most beautiful amber light that lit up the nearby creek bed like it was a floodlight on a stage set. She did her usual scientific looking-around to try to make sense of it, but the sun had set a half hour before and there was no way a beam of natural light could have reached the space at that hour of the day. It was lightning, yes, but it lingered much longer than a mere bolt. Like so many miracles from Rainbow Bridge, it can't really be described.

As soon as the light came, the thunder rolled from one side of the valley to the other. I knew how she loved the thunder and I wanted her to have some. I wanted to make her happy. The thunder rumbled long and deep. Then it rolled high as it traveled up over the nearby mesa. Wild Horse Mesa. The one she always loved so much.

I know she now knows the truth. I was the thunder. I was the lightning too. I knew she knew it was me because when she said, "Thank you Thank you Jack" she was crying because she knew in her heart that those things were my response to her.

And the brave mourning dove that becomes uneasy with such things and often flies away in fear, well she remained in the nearby tree and stayed for the whole show. She was no ordinary dove. She was an angel who came to help Kate say goodbye to her mourning.

I was the hummingbird. I was the thunder, the lightning; I came in my light and my vibration.

When You Least Expect It...

It was an unseasonably warm winter day. The sun was shining bright and its soft filtered light set the landscape all aglow. She and Joey were at the park, exploring the rugged dirt path that led down to the river. The loamy trail extended just beyond Grandfather Tree and then it turned sandy as it meandered for several miles along the reedy banks.

It took them both by surprise when a Golden Retriever came running from out of nowhere towards them at top speed with tail wagging. It was headed straight for Joey.

"Don't worry about that old boy," a voice called out. "He's just happy to see one of his own kind."

A handsome cowboy appeared around the backside of a huge sycamore tree. He tipped his hat, just like they do in the old movies. He introduced himself as Shane Robertson. On foot, he was leading his chestnut mare behind him.

"Just call me Shane," he said. "Hey," he asked. "Is there any chance you've seen four cows in your travels? They've wandered off from the rest of the group..."

"Sorry no, I haven't seen any cows," she answered.

"What brings you out to these parts?" he asked and before she could answer he added with a wink, "...and would you like to join me for dinner tonight?"

She was taken aback by his confident invitation. His smile was charming; his eyes were bright. He looked a generation older than she but his deep crow's feet gave intense character to his face and he was in better physical shape than most people a generation behind.

She couldn't take her eyes off the Carhartt logo on the jacket that he was wearing. She thought of her recent conversation with Barbara and she surprised me by accepting his invitation. I think the jacket was the clincher.

They went out to dinner a few times. He took her to the finest places and seemed a perfect gentleman. He bought her flowers and expensive presents. Held her coat for her and pulled her chair out for her. She was overwhelmed with his kindness and generosity. He was definitely courting her.

A couple of weeks later he gave her a full tour of his giant riverside ranch as he recited to her all that he had to offer. It was an impressive lineup. It was not long before he wanted to marry her. Three weeks I think.

I didn't particularly care for him. I was very protective of her and I knew how vulnerable she was, even though she showed everyone the side of her that was strong, the side of her that didn't need anyone or anything. This was the magnet that attracted him. He didn't want another needy woman. Meanwhile she rationalized that he was a "good catch".

What does your heart say?

Shane had money, rugged good looks, manners and an appreciation of the nature that surrounded him. He was smart and he stimulated her intellect. She had never been very impressed with material things, ambition or physical attributes, although they certainly scored some points. It was all because of the Carhartt jacket. The seed had been planted and she felt that it was a "sign". A sign that was letting her know this was the guy for her. Sometimes when you believe in signs, you can think something is a sign when it's just a random occurrence...but there are reasons for everything nonetheless! What I noticed right away is that she didn't seem to feel any genuine love for him in her heart. She may have been thinking she needed a new life, but she didn't need a new life. She just needed the right life.

She had always before been drawn into relationship by feelings of love and chemistry, but this time she was looking at everything from a very practical standpoint. She was looking at love and partnership from her head and not her heart. True love is not practical. True love doesn't always follow the rules. When you are truly in love, you can lose your mind over it.

We Come in Dreams

Between soul mates, love knows no bounds. The abilities of the soul are unlimited. You can travel simply by opening your mind and heart and focusing your thoughts. You can travel in your dreams and have all kinds of amazing experiences.

I came to her most nights in dreams, but she doesn't remember some of them. That's okay. Dreams take place in the subconscious mind, so even if she can't remember the actual dream, her soul remembers. Her soul is her higher self and her higher self and mine are directly connected. Her soul learns and helps her to apply what I have shared with her there.

A dream we had last night was difficult for her to grasp. It was kind of normal but it was also kind of distressing for her. In her distress she turned to me and I was there with her and because of that, everything was okay. I was just letting her know that I am always with her and not to be too stressed about anything because nothing in this world really matters.

When she awakened from our dream, she tried for a little while to remember it but she couldn't. Even so, she smiled and said my name. I love it when she says my name.

"Jack. I dreamed of Jack."

She knew I had been there and she knew that there was nothing at all to be stressed about. I knew in this moment that she would be receptive to hearing me speak to her.

I want you to love again. I want you to be loved as much as you loved me.

She shed more tears. Not so much the tears of grief as the tears of realizing the truth. Then goose bumps.

"I saw you Jack. I saw you last night."

I know you know that I was there.

"You were running so fast, like a gazelle! You were so beautiful. You are."

When I am running in your dreams, I am running to you. Running on the wings of your love for me.

"I knew the first moment I saw you. Remember, Jack? I said 'He's the one.' And you were. You were the one for me."

A Lesson in Vibration

She must have been pretty serious about Shane because she took him home to meet her mother. At one point Shane left the house to go to the village gas station. He went to get gas but he was really leaving to get a break from the intensity of her mother. He had a low tolerance for most women. Kate and her mother then had some much needed time together.

"When you get old enough to take care of yourself, as you have, it takes a very special man to replace no man at all," said her mother, who was committed only to never getting married again.

It was another message for Kate. It can be easy for an adult woman to disregard her mother's advice, but she had to admit her mother had been right about many things.

"Men will either pull you down or you will pull them up. I don't see you pulling him up. I think he is the one who has the control. You're too easy on him." On and on she went. "Birds of a feather flock together." "Like attracts like and he isn't like you."

Once again, her mother was right. Shane was bringing her down to his level. She was compromising herself, giving her power away to him. Making what he wanted more important than what she wanted.

The longer Kate was with Shane the more controlling he became. She had been working on it, but she hadn't broken it off yet. She was staying in the old shoe. Some people feel better having something than nothing. I was sorry that she was this way because when you make room for something else by letting go of something that doesn't work for you, God has a chance of bringing in miracles.

It wasn't that he didn't love her because he told her all the time that he did. What I didn't like about him was that he didn't show her that he loved her and actions speak louder than words.

Her friends kept asking about him. They wanted to see her in a relationship that made her happy. After all, the only "date" she ever took with her in those eight years was me.

Loyalty

She wasn't 100% healed yet. It was not a good time to make a life-changing decision. When one feels vulnerable, they are especially attracted to someone or something that shows hope of saving them from their own lives. She still was grieving and that is why she didn't want to live her own life. I think she thought the grief was over and because she still wasn't happy, she thought maybe Shane could make her happy. She didn't know the grief would eventually end and when it did she would not want him anymore.

She wanted to fill the hole that she thought was in her heart with something else, anything else, so she wouldn't feel the hole. Shane was the one who happened to be there.

The real issue was that she was still looking for everything she needed outside of herself. She didn't realize that when she finally healed, the hole she had felt in her heart would be gone.

You can't "make" someone your soul mate. You can try but it will always be very hard work. Human relationships are hard even when they are easy, so it's important to be in one with a soul mate. She felt she could learn to love Shane; that she might grow to love him over time. She always felt she could make her mind up and then accomplish anything, but the heart and the mind have different agendas. If she was going to try to make this relationship work, it had to come from her heart, not from 'making up her mind'. You don't have to "try" to be anything when you are with your soul mate because they are looking for who you are, not for who you are trying to be.

She wasn't his soul mate either, even though he said that she was. I could see into his heart just like God can see into every heart. What Shane really wanted was a helpmate, ranch hand, cook, and caregiver when he got old, which wasn't far off. He had been widowed, his kids were grown and he had his own gaping hole in his own heart. He was trying to fill it up with her.

I knew I would have to step in to help her to manage the situation. Life is too short --and too long-- to be with someone who doesn't touch your heart and soul.

I knew it was all by Design. Because everything is.

Surrendering Sammi

New friends come into your life for a reason. Don't run from them. They aren't always another soul mate, but they need you to need them and they are your helpmates. They have come to teach you the next advanced levels of love lessons. They are often the bridge to your healing.

Animals don't judge and we ask you now to also keep an open mind as I share this chapter with you. She doesn't want me to share it but that's because she still feels guilt and she still feels pain over it. She knows that animal rights activists can react and attack. I am striving to prove to her that by sharing this with you, she can find out that compassion can exist for such things as she has done.

She had seen it all too many times: a person or a family who gave up a dog or cat or other pet because they no longer had the money to care for it. "So get another job," she would say to them. Or "Why would you even adopt a pet if you thought you wouldn't be able to care for it for the long haul?"

Then there were those who would move from one house to another. "They don't allow pets where we're moving," they would say and put their pet up for adoption or drop the pet off at the local shelter. "So get a house that allows pets!" She would react vehemently, "Why would you get a pet and then move to a house that doesn't allow it?" She saw every pet as a family member. Each one was a commitment for life.

People often judge what they don't understand. She did not understand until her own life brought her to her knees and she found a new compassion for others.

There is a dog you never heard her talk too much about. The story started several years ago and, until just a few weeks ago, she was filled with such guilt and shame.

Sammi was born the runt of the litter. At the time Kate was coming off being very sick and she had put her house on the market. The realtor's female German shepherd had just had a litter of eleven pups and she invited Kate over to see them.

"If I go see them I'm going to want one," Kate said to her.

Kate went over to see them. She didn't want one. She wanted all of them. Two already had homes. Kate went over almost every day. Sometimes she took me with her and it was fun. They followed me around like ducklings running after their mother. I also had a bit of a crush on the beautiful white shepherd who had given birth to them four weeks before.

She fell in love with the litter as she trained them all to sit for a biscuit at the age of five weeks. Every single one of them had their butt on the ground waiting for the milk bone. They were so smart!

The day came and the realtor called Kate. It wasn't about the house. It was about the pups. Two of them had found homes, leaving nine more. A couple more would be purchased over the next week or so.

"If I can't get rid of the rest of them by next Monday, they are going to the Humane Society."

Kate was horrified. She emailed everyone she knew and she put an ad on Facebook. She made some phone calls. By Monday she had found homes for all of them but one. Sammi.

Sammi was hers. She was good-natured with a healthy appetite. She played really well with me and she was a good student too. I taught her many things that Kate could not teach her. Kate took her to Obedience Training at the park and Sammi learned everything really fast. She loved her toys, she loved me, and she loved Kate. She made our world a happy and active place.

Then the house sold and Kate had to find another place to live. She didn't have much money because she had been sick and didn't have a lot to work with. A friend was moving out of state and asked Kate to housesit for her for an extended time. Kate jumped at the chance. We started moving in and then we found out that only one large dog was allowed to live there. The wheels were already in motion and it seemed too late to find an alternative.

Sammi was nine months old by now and a perfect lady. She was obedient, healthy and above all, love-able. Kate's heart fell as she made the necessary calls. She quickly found a home for Sammi in a nearby town. Sammi's new home was a big ranch house with a fenced-in acre of lush green grass with a lovely family and another dog for company. Every week we used to go to see Sammi. Every once in awhile Kate would say to the family, "If you ever think about letting Sammi go, please call me first." After all, she wouldn't be housesitting forever.

"Oh, she's not going anywhere," the husband would reply, "She's part of our family now."

Like everything else, over time we adjust. We started visiting Sammi every month. Then every other month. When I crossed Rainbow Bridge, it had been nearly a year since we'd seen Sammi. A short time later, Kate contacted the family just to check in to see if Sammi was still there. She had room for a big dog again.

Well, they had moved and they didn't even have Sammi anymore! They had found another home for her. Oh Kate was so upset! She knew she really had no right to be upset, but she wanted Sammi to have a "stable" home life. She didn't like the thought that Sammi had been adopted out a second time.

"Why didn't they call ME? I TOLD them to call ME," she cried. Once again, she learned that nothing is certain.

Circumstances can change just as they had changed for her.

She had learned from Joey and from her own life about abandonment issues. It's what made her so sensitive to Sammi's plight. It took her a very long time to get over it. She couldn't seem to accept the fact that there are reasons for everything.

That is, until just a few weeks ago. She was driving in the city and had stopped at a traffic light. She glanced over at the sedan that had pulled up into the right-hand lane beside her. It was an undercover patrol car. Painted in beautiful gold letters on the back door was "S-A-M-M-I" and there was a gorgeous adult German shepherd sitting obediently in the back seat behind the grilled partition. She couldn't believe her eyes. She tried to keep up with the car from light to light. She tried to get a picture of it because sometimes a photo will help you to believe something that your mind can confuse.

No matter. It was another example of destiny. Fate. Sammi needed to be in the right place at the right time. She had been well trained for an important reason: for the K-9 Division. Some time later, Kate found out that a senior police dog had retired and Sammi just happened to be in the right place at the right time. Once Kate saw the result of her actions and that the outcome was a good one, Kate could put her tormenting thoughts to rest. She could finally stop blaming herself for abandoning her dog when she realized that she was just a pawn in the game of

Sammi's life. Once again, it was all part of the plan. The other family was part of the plan too.

Some humans are so consumed with trying to control the outcomes of their own lives that they don't have any idea the part they play in the outcome of someone else's.

Seeds of Change

One of the tasks I was given when I came across the Rainbow Bridge was to choose a dog on earth to serve as its Guardian Angel. I had to leave earth but I, in turn, was to compensate for my departure. Our Master never takes something away without filling the space it left behind. I jumped at the chance because I thought it would be fun to see if I could bring another dog and Kate together.

I knew that she would probably want a bigger dog and I just seemed to know that she would eventually want an Afghan Hound. It's how everything was panning out. I did my research. There are only about five hundred Afghan Hounds born in the United States each year. It is a rare and unique breed.

It did not take long. I found the right one. Immy was a purebred Afghan Hound who had failed the show circuit, couldn't earn her keep, and would need a home soon. The timing wasn't quite right yet.

It became my mission to bring the two of them together. Somehow. Someway. I didn't know how I would go about it, with Kate in Arizona and Immy in Montana and all, but I knew that with my Master's help, it would be done.

One day late in the winter season Kate's friend Jane sent a photo of an Afghan Hound who needed a home. "This may be an Afghan Hound for you," Jane said.

"Oh Jane he is beautiful, but I don't think I want an Afghan Hound," Kate said frowning. "In fact I'm not ready to even think about another dog."

She was right. She wasn't ready. After that, every so often she'd find herself thinking about it. That's how it works, the pulling forward. Ironically, thoughts of me would interrupt her thoughts of getting another dog and it would bring feelings of guilt upon her. Those thoughts would bring her right back to feeling like she couldn't move forward. Meanwhile I was urging her to move forward so I could complete my task.

Sometimes she'd mention getting another dog to someone and they would tell her, "No, it's too soon." Most of them didn't understand the relationship we had and most of them wanted her to be free from the obligation and responsibility of having to take care of "another big dog". Whatever the reasons, she would not be ready until she was ready. The day she is ready it won't matter what anyone tells her. She will go.

It was coming time for her to learn new lessons and she would need a new kind of dog. It's how it is Designed. Each dog brings different tasks to their human to be completed. In return, our human raises us to the next level. The more we are treated like a trusted friend, the greater our capabilities.

Keep in mind that if you give us a human name, it will make us more human. If you treat us more like a human than a pet, it will further us in ways you never dreamed of! We will be more evolved than most four-leggeds. Each one of us is an invitation to you to love more, be more, give more, receive more, and understand more. Each one of us is an invitation to you to become so much more than you ever were before.

Jane was very persistent. She kept sending Kate messages every week or two advertising Afghan Hounds who needed homes.

"No thank you," Kate would say as she cast them aside.

It's really like a treasure hunt how we find each other. One thing leads to another leads to another. Little did she know her friend Jane had planted the seed. She planted it for her. She planted it for me.

It's never "too soon" or "too late" if there is a new friend you resonate with. Try not to judge yourself. Your best friend is not judging you. Your best friend who watches over you just wants you to be happy again. You simply need to be in the right place at the right time to get the one who is right for you. The day may come and you will feel an unexpected desire to act. While certain things are out of your control, there is a certain responsibility you have to act on your urges and wants, which are there for a reason: to propel you towards your heart's desire.

The Best Things Aren't Things

She had become more and more unhappy in her relationship with Shane, but she was still making the best of things. She thought him inflexible, critical and arrogant. At the same time, she was so loyal it made me think that she must have been a dog in a previous life.

You're not supposed to be with him.

Shane was like a spoiled little boy who surrounded himself with adult playthings to create his world. Like a child in a sandbox, he moved land, he built structures, he had farm animals and trucks and tractors and four wheelers. He even had an airplane in a hangar the next town over. He had lots and lots of money too! But he didn't have very many friends and that's really what concerned me the most. He could take care of his machines but he didn't know how to take care of a relationship. He always bought whatever he wanted and he usually bought his women too, thinking the money would be enough. It had always been enough before.

Humans are funny. The more someone doesn't want someone, the more that someone wants that someone. The time came when she started pulling away. She had developed a tendency to focus on the things that she didn't respect in him and eventually that's all she saw. A man needs to be respected and a woman needs to feel loved and both of them were coming up short. I could have told her that a long time ago; in fact I did. As soon as she started pulling away, he wanted to see her all the time. He told her he'd fly her wherever she wanted to go in his private plane.

Whenever she thought about breaking it off, she would tend to find some inherently good qualities in him but when she searched her heart to find the love she had for him it was not there.

When you have experienced love on a very deep level, no other kind of love will do. Once you've healed, you'd rather have no love at all. She was almost there.

Irreplaceable

At any given time there are many thousands of dogs, cats and other orphaned pets waiting for homes. She was looking online at all of them.

Some were on death row, like Joey had been. Some were being fostered and cared for by devoted rescue groups. There were so many needing homes and Kate found herself wanting to adopt every single one of them. She even briefly considered the fantasy of fostering and surrounding herself with all the pets in the world that needed love. Remember, we always want to give another what we wish for ourselves.

"I guess I'm just not ready."

She felt stuck. She couldn't look forward because she kept looking back. She didn't have room in her heart for new love because her weak feelings for Shane were still taking up space in there. Plus, she wasn't quite done grieving me.

The search for another dog was simply her effort to try to find another me. She would not be ready to love another in a healthy way until she stopped comparing everyone to me. It's impossible to go out and find someone that you already have!

The search went on for a long time. As winter turned to spring, her wish for another dog became stronger and stronger. She was feeling pressured to find a dog before the heat of summer came so that she could leave Joey at home instead of leaving him in her hot car. The summer was my friend!

For many nights in a row, she spent hours searching online. It had become a bit of an obsession. This is how you know you are getting ready. You don't give up. She was committed to finding an Afghan Hound.

At the time there were only six Afghan Hounds listed on the rescue site. Two of them were simply too far away and the others needed to be placed as pairs together in their new home. One night she extended her search to a site where breeders list puppies. She never imagined buying a purebred puppy from a breeder so she went onto the site not really expecting anything. She was still planning on rescuing one. After all, that's what she'd always done and we all tend to do what we've always done before.

As she browsed through the dogs, she fell instantly in love with a nine month old Afghan Hound named "Miss Green Collar". I know why she fell in love with her. I'm the one who coordinated it because I knew what she was looking for. Not only did Miss Green Collar have the same color collar I always wore, it was mostly the look in her eyes. It was the way I would look at Kate. The eyes are the windows to the soul and Green Collar's eyes were the attraction for Kate.

They haunted Kate's thoughts, morning till night and they filled her dreams. Those eyes were the magnets that would come to draw Kate to Montana.

Little did she know how much work was still ahead of her with our book. She would push Miss Green Collar out of her thoughts but Miss Green Collar would continually creep back in. Then the guilty feelings would come because she was looking at another dog instead of me and she felt that she was being disloyal to me. She was not.

I needed her to follow the Plan.

New Goals, New Life

It was February. She wrote the breeder in Montana, inquiring about Miss Green Collar. The siblings, Miss Red Collar, Miss Blue Collar and Miss Light Green Collar were available too, but Kate only had eyes for the Green Collared girl.

The breeder, Brian, was patient and helpful as they corresponded over the weeks. Kate had a lot of questions and concerns. Brian's honesty, knowledge and forthrightness made it easy for her to trust him, but she just couldn't seem to move forward.

At one point Brian laughed and said to her, "Of course, if you wait long enough, someone else will get her."

She couldn't go to see Miss Green Collar until she finished my book! I told her so. My old friend Lizard arrived on the scene to help ensure that she did not leave ahead of her time. There was a very good reason. The conditions weren't right.

"When I'm done with Jack's book," she told herself, "I'll go to Montana and get that girl. I'll go get Miss Green Collar."

She finished our book the first of April. It then took her the better part of another month to create the cover and to get the manuscript formatted. She had to learn

Microsoft Word after having used it for twenty years, never knowing what it was capable of. It was all by design, the timing of it all. I needed her to write our book and I needed to delay her trip to Montana.

She was rushing to get the book published by her goal date of May first. I don't know why she always set deadlines like that for herself, but I knew her well and it made it possible for me to schedule what I had to do.

The day ultimately came when she called Brian to give him her date of arrival. That was the day she learned that Miss Green Collar had found another home. She was surprised by her reaction. She didn't even possess Miss Green Collar and yet she cried bitterly as if she had lost her. She had become very attached to the thought of her. The power of her own emotions surprised her but I know why she cried like that. She cried because she wasn't finished grieving the loss of me. When someone has an exaggerated emotional reaction to something in the present, it's usually because they haven't resolved something in their past.

Meanwhile Miss Green Collar's two sisters, Miss Red Collar and Miss Blue Collar, were still available, as well as an older boy. She mulled this over. Over time she had become strangely attached to Brian and his dogs.

She kept the plan in place. Kate finished our book on the first of May and a few days later she was on the road to

Montana with little Joey. It was a twenty plus hour road trip each way. I was glad she was going, for many reasons. She had worked very hard on our book and it was a good change of pace. It allowed for special 1:1 time with Joey, who had been waiting patiently for her to prioritize him. Most of all it was something new for her. New roads, new people, new places, new opportunities and new perspective. This is the one thing that inevitably moves a person through the grief. Growth heals grief.

The Heart Will Lead

I rode right along with them to Montana, but it's funny how she didn't seem to be looking for me as much there. She was looking ahead. If she looked behind, she would find herself grieving over Miss Green Collar instead of me. Looking ahead, she was imagining the remaining Afghan Hounds who needed homes. She was finally moving forward. It was a lot more fun for me to be with her when she was this way.

They had reserved a little rustic cabin for the week. Located in a sleepy little ranch town, it was surrounded by sunlit farmlands with cattle and buffalo roaming nearby. Less than a mile away from the cabin lived the breeder.

She arrived quite late in the evening. When she called Brian that night, she learned that, not only was Miss Green Collar gone, but Miss Red Collar and Miss Blue Collar had left for new homes too! All of the girls from that litter were now gone, after many months of not being claimed. She was disappointed to say the least.

"Why? Why did I come all this way?"

I knew why. She didn't know it yet, but God and I, well, we had something else in mind for her.

The next morning, she and Joey drove over to meet Brian and his Afghan Hound family. She had seen the distant red farmhouse in photos but it was exciting to see it come into three-dimensional view. With eighty acres of invisible fencing, it was bordered by the river, with rolling hills and surrounded by nature as far as the eye could see. It seemed a generous slice of God's country. She was in awe of the beauty there.

That was just the beginning. She pulled into the driveway and entered another world. She found herself in Afghan Hound Heaven...on earth that is. As they got out of the car, the female hounds hovered around and welcomed them. The boys were in a separate area, roughhousing.

Kate and Joey waited at the front gate to meet the boys. One of the girls trailed behind Kate to get her scent. She pawed the back of Kate's leg, but Kate never noticed her there. She was too busy looking at the boys romping around on the grass on the other side, trying to guess which boy was the one that was available.

Breeder Brian opened the gate and welcomed them and Joey joined them in a game of Afghan Zoomies. Oh it was so much fun to see them having so much fun! Joey needed this kind of playtime after so many somber months with her.

Brian then took Kate to the back of the house. Georgie was the boy who needed a home. Georgie was lying on a little hillside all by himself under a tiny shade tree. Nearby,

Immy was hanging out at the corner of the yard. Kate was supposed to ask about Immy, but Kate didn't even notice Immy she was so busy looking at Georgie.

"Well, this is Georgie," said Brian, introducing them.

"He's beautiful!" She admired Georgie's dark hair, tan spaniel dots over his eyes and his stunning physique.

No. I kept saying. *Not him.*

"How old is he?"

No, not Georgie. He's not the right one.

"He's two and a half," said Breeder Brian. "He had a home but the couple broke up and neither one of them could keep him."

I was speaking from my heart to hers. I had said the same thing when she came to the puppy mill and was preparing to take my brother home with her. She heard me then. Would she hear me now?

You don't want him. Look around you.

"How could anyone let him go?" she asked Brian.

He shrugged. "Owners will do what owners will do."

They spent some time with the big gentle soul. Georgie was obedient, easy-going, a perfect gentleman. They went for a walk on the leash and he was easy to guide. Then they sat inside on the couch with him.

There's someone else who wants you.

Georgie was calm and receptive to her touch. He was so soft!

There's someone else who needs you.

141

He was a very sweet boy. It seemed perfect somehow but somehow it wasn't. Kate didn't understand. She didn't know what was missing. Something was missing. She thought how the first little black pup with the green collar was long gone; now living in Ohio. The little black sibling girls were all gone too. She had driven all these miles, all these hours. Could she leave empty-handed when there was no excuse not to take Georgie home with her?

You're not meant to have Georgie.

"I love Georgie," she said to Brian. "I wish I could tell you that he feels like the right dog for me but..." She simply couldn't put a finger on it.

Someone else is waiting for him.

After a long silence, Brian said, "Well... there is one other girl that I'm willing to have you take a look at."

We're almost there.

Enter Immy. She loved Immy in an instant. Not quite the same way she loved me when she met me but, after all, it's going to be different this time around. Immy was small and beautiful. She wasn't without her quirks. She was shy, anxious and mistrustful. She had failed the show dog circuit; known as, "Better Luck Next Time."

I could read her heart. Immy knew she was pretty but she did not know that she had anything else to offer. Kate would soon witness the wildness that ran through Immy's blood and how she would run from

142

love. Immy would be a challenge. After all, I had been so easy for Kate for so long.

"She feels right to me but I wonder if I feel right to her." I was glad she was thinking about how Immy was feeling about it.

"I think she already chose you," Brian stated with certainty. "Didn't you notice how she put her paw on the back of your leg when you arrived here today?"

She had not noticed. She had been too busy looking at all the other dogs, wondering which one was going to be hers.

She is your mirror. There are parts of you she is showing you. Parts of you now hidden even from your own awareness. You will help her and she will help you and you both will come out of this stronger because of each other.

Knowing the situation, I knew that Breeder Brian had not been willing to relinquish Immy until that very moment. He wasn't supposed to. It was part of The Plan. Had this played out any differently, I think she might have taken Georgie home. Or then again she might not have.

I'm glad she didn't because she would have interfered with Georgie's destiny. In fact it was interesting when, a few months later, the woman who had Georgie's biological sister contacted Brian looking for another mature dog. Georgie was then able to go to a loving home with his birth sister, where he was supposed to be.

Unlike Kate, I waste no time on "What Might Have Been" because what happened was what was Meant To Be. It needed to play out this way because I was assigned to this mission long before Kate ever started looking at dogs. I brought the best possible friend for her to learn the lessons that she would need to move forward towards becoming all that she could be.

No Dogs Allowed

She found herself taking more and more time away from Shane. She was in a new love relationship now: the shared love of her "children", Immy and Joey. Shane didn't seem particularly interested in the dogs and yet he was driven by his insecurity and his jealousy of Immy. When he spoke of Immy everything was condescending and critical. A person will sometimes minimize someone else in an effort to make themselves look better. Case in point.

"Her head's too small for her brain...she's going to be an aggressive dog...she's too skittish...imbalanced...too much hair...too much attitude..."

It was no surprise to me when Shane got down on bended knee one evening, as chivalrous men will do, and asked her to marry him.

"There's only one rule," he added, "and one rule only." He told her that he would have to enforce it: "NO DOGS ON THE BED!" It kind of interrupted the romantic moment.

It simply was not acceptable to her. She never wanted to reject him so she found the kindest sweetest way to tell him "no." He glared at her for a moment in response and then waived a finger inches from her face and said in a snide voice, "After all I've done for you!"

It was not the first time she had heard those words and it was how she knew she was making the right decision. The funny thing is, she never ever asked him for anything yet he was holding her accountable for everything he had ever given her. Why do people do that? Maybe they don't feel worthy of love or they grew up learning to control everything with money. That's not really giving at all. It's buying. He was trying to buy her. He couldn't. After all, she was priceless if you ask me.

As she arrived home that night Barbara was calling. 'How are things going with Shane? Wow. What a great catch!'

She had to tell Barbara the story.

They are now sleeping in bed comfortably together in eternal bliss: Kate and Immy and Joey.

Liquid Love

I watched her turn the calendar pages. Time was passing. The roses had faded, shedding their soft petals so that they could return vibrant and full of color in their next season of life.

The snows came. The afternoons were dark; the mornings were darker. By spring she had made progress. Everyone who grieves does eventually. It may take a season or a year or more; everyone goes at their own pace. It is the body's nature to heal a wound and it is the spirit's nature to heal from the throes of grief.

She would say to me, "Look at me Jack, I'm still crying over you! Why? I have Immy now. I have Joey. I'm really very happy. If that's true, then why am I still crying over you?"

I know you still love me. I still see you cry when you don't think you have everything, but you do. You have Joey. You have Immy. You have me. You do have everything.

Some people cry for a little while – some cry for a long time. Tears are an important release. If tears are not shed, they take up valuable space and block one's ability to heal. Tears literally wash the grief away.

Finally the day came and her tears were very different. They had become slow giant tears that took a long time to come out of her eyes and then slide down her cheek. They were heavy with love. They were tears made of her love for me, sweet where they once were bitter. The sweetness had come with time and acceptance.

It's human nature to heal and she was getting ready to be free from all sadness and grief. The smiles would come and gentle laughter too. The tears would go. The first time she would realize that she had smiled without the tears would be the beginning of becoming who I taught her to be. She would be ready soon.

Once Kate healed, Immy was able to stand on her own four feet having accepted her life with Kate and Joey. Teaching each other lessons in love, they were reaching the point where they no longer needed me. I had some mixed feelings about that, for we all want to be needed. When our energy is healthy, we always want a challenge. We want to keep learning and loving and exploring the universe.

Little did I know what was coming.

The Meeting

All the stars were in alignment and I had arranged The Meeting. After dinner she would find him there. Blue eyes. Salt and Pepper hair. It's not that I was so interested in getting her out to a bar, but there are just so many places on earth for people to meet people.

She was doing much better; holding her own. She seemed to be smiling and laughing a lot, more like her old self. It was fun for me to see her this way and it helped me to know that soon, very soon, while she would never forget me, she would no longer feel that aching gaping hole in her heart.

They had placed their orders and her friend Caroline returned from the bar area with a drink.

"There's this guy over there you need to meet," she said to Kate. "He works over at our office. I've seen him in the lunch room."

Kate's best friends always seemed to look out for her. The others at the table were all paired up and while they didn't understand her deep grief over losing me, they also did not want to see her forever moving through her life alone.

"Hey Kate," said Caroline's husband Jim, "While you're up there can you grab me a draft?"

"Wait, I'll go with you!" Caroline said cheerfully, winking at Jim as she slid her arm through Kate's arm to guide her to the bar.

At the bar, they ordered the drinks and then Caroline brought "Brad" over to meet Kate.

No, I said to her, *that's not the right guy.*

Salt and Pepper was just finishing dinner with a couple at a table right near their dinner table. I was kind of new at this and I thought that was all I had to do.

"How do you do?" She made the first move, extending her hand to Brad. His hand felt limp and damp and she said to herself, "No. This isn't the right guy."

While she followed Caroline back to the table, I was coming to realize how many things can get in the way of other things.

Just as they were approaching their table, Salt and Pepper pushed his chair back to get up and it blocked her path. Such fun! I hope she sees his Carhartt jacket!

"Oops!" She was surprised. The collision caused her to spill some of the drink that she was carrying.

"Oh I'm sorry," he said, "I wasn't paying attention." He looked at her with kindness.

"It's okay. No harm done."

She looked back at him, wondering where she had seen him before. She felt his eyes piercing her heart. The moment commanded her full attention.

Glancing over at his table, she nodded hello to the man and woman who were sitting there. They didn't look very happy. Wow, she thought to herself as her eyes returned to his. Who wouldn't be happy having dinner with him?

"Do I know you?" she asked, finding him more familiar than he seemed at first glance.

"I don't think so," was his reply.

She looked back at the couple dining with him, felt their disapproval and decided to move along.

"Well," said Kate excusing herself, "It was nice seeing you."

Back at the table, as the chatter went on around her, her mind kept going to Salt and Pepper. She glanced over at him. He seemed like a very nice person. He was handsome in a rugged kind of way.

"So why did you choose Sedona?" Jim asked her, drawing her attention back to her own table. "You were so brave and courageous to make such a move all by yourself!"

"I didn't move all by myself. I had Grady with me," she replied.

"You mean you didn't know anyone there?" Patty stated, "Were you crazy?" All but Caroline looked at her like she had three heads.

"When the Spirit moves you unexpectedly and you can't find a reason that makes any sense," Caroline commented, "the underlying reason is love and only love."

Caroline was right, for there are many Helpers behind the scenes pulling strings and making things happen so that you can be where you need to be and grow and love and live and learn.

Even Kate felt that perhaps she should have questioned her sanity back then, moving 3000 miles away from her hometown and all, but she had felt driven to start a new life. She didn't know why, only that she had to go. It was like she had no choice.

She couldn't answer them. She didn't feel particularly brave or courageous. There had been no practical reason for the move to Arizona. She had thought that perhaps The Love of Her Life would be found there. She couldn't come up with any other reason that made any sense.

She was right. He was. He was there. He was me! All the while as she was imagining the handsome cowboy or bright post-graduate student who would cross her path, I was positioning myself to be hers. That's why she came to Sedona so she could find me and know me and love me and write this book so that you could know me too and so I'd know you.

Salt and Pepper's table raised their glasses in toast and as they did, Kate saw a glimpse of wedding band. She looked away quickly, so as not to be caught staring.

"Oh my gosh," she said to herself. "I hope he didn't think I was flirting with him! I hope they didn't think I was flirting with him!"

I wish you didn't worry so much about what other people think.

Her thoughts traveled to me, then traveled home to Immy and Joey, then traveled back to me. They traveled back to the man with the salt and pepper hair. She looked over at his table as they were getting up to leave. Kate had started getting a little distressed by the drunken conversation going on at her own table and realized it was getting to be time for her to leave too. Until she was done healing she would never really feel like she fit in with the rest of the crowd.

She excused herself. "I'm sorry guys but it's getting late for me and I have an early morning tomorrow."

Yes. That's good. Keep going.

Salt and Pepper and his friends had just left the restaurant. She had to walk through the bar to go out to her car. There was a small group of people there that she knew from hospice who were her friends from work. She stopped to talk with them.

No. Don't stop.

Outside it had started pouring rain and Salt and Pepper was standing at the front door under the awning waiting for the rain to stop. I brought the man. I brought the rain. I brought the moment. I did not bring the group from hospice that delayed her passage to the front door. I don't make the plans; I just facilitate them. So I wasn't sure what the plan was supposed to be now that this had not come to pass.

———

153

That night she became reacquainted with a young man from the legal firm in town by the name of Benjamin. She knew him from his pro bono work with hospice. He was handsome and generous and had very good manners. The best part was that he treated her nice. He was genuine.

She had been learning her love lessons all along the way. Loving me had raised the bar for what was acceptable to her. It wasn't Salt And Pepper, but there are at any given time several soul mates in the world looking one for the other, so I knew it was time for me to let it go. When there are obstacles like this, it is either the wrong time or the wrong place or the wrong person. If something is meant to be, it's simply meant to be and it will be right.

As I watched Benjamin hold the door for her and praise her for the wonderful woman she was, I knew it was time. I knew that she had someone who cared. I saw their potential. She was no longer alone. I saw that the hole in her heart that had been filled with the love and then the loss of me was now healed and was filling with feelings of care for this man. It was time for goodbye but I was not sad. I knew that she and I would meet again and that all of this that was happening would pass in the blink of an eye.

She was getting stronger. I could see it clearly. I could feel it. It made me so happy that she felt strong and happy too. It was the most important thing to me and it still is. The stronger she is the stronger I can be.

"I'm so glad you never had to get old," she was now saying to me. She still thought of me each day but in a more balanced way. She wasn't obsessed with my absence any more.

"Thank you for being mine, Jack. I'm glad I had you, if only for a little while. "

Thank you for being mine.

She was healed.

I would be able to move forward very soon.

Answering the Call

My Master interrupted my thoughts as He called me in from the fields of green and gold. His voice was commanding and I ran to Him obediently. When I lived upon the earth, she was everything to me, but when I went Home, He became my everything. I knew He loved me too and I would always run to Him, eager to please, because we loved each other so. She taught me to live this way upon the earth so that I would be prepared for my life with Him here.

He gave me a choice: To remain here and continue living life as an angel in Heaven, or to return to Earth. Not everyone gets to stay in Heaven forever, but He said I could stay forever if I wanted to. Heaven offers an easy life, free and joyous. I earned it by being such a good student of my earthly lessons of love. It was not required of me to go back to learn more, but I could choose to go back if I wanted to serve and teach.

I hesitated. After all, life in Heaven is wonderful. We can do whatever we want to do. We'll have a little dream of you. We'll take a lovely walk through the Rainbow Fields and think of you. We'll teach a Rainbow class based on what we learned from you. We'll join together for Rainbow games and later on we'll think of you. We take the long way home most days, just so we can keep watch at the gate to see if you're coming, but it's going to be a little while. After work and after play we all sit around and talk about our favorite people just like you sit around and talk about us. Why would I ever want to leave?

I told my Master I did not want to leave Heaven. Most of all, I didn't want to be somewhere else the day she crossed over the Rainbow Bridge. I wanted to be the first one at the edge of the Bridge to greet her. It was a dream for me, our souls reunited in our true Forever Home!

I decided to wait for her. My memories were strong. I could go to her anytime. I could have it all. There is no love like the love we shared. Our love could not be repeated. She was my heart and my soul and my vivid memories lived right there within her. So that is why I decided that I would wait. I thanked Him and told him that I would rather wait for her.

No, I think I will wait. Thank you.

He would never tell me what to do. He would only help me to find my own answers. This time He gave me another chance.

ARE YOU SURE?

He explained to me that I had attained a certain status where not only could I choose to go back as a dog, but I could even choose to go back as a human...or of course I could still choose to not go back at all.

I'm sure He knew as He told me this that my mind would entertain for just a moment what it would be like to be human. He knew I would think about returning to live my life upon the earth to access the delicious pleasures available to me there. He knew that this would open the door to the possibilities.

In Heaven it's easy to say goodbye because we know that everything happens in the blink of an eye and we know that we will soon be reunited again. Everyone has faith in Heaven and faith is what makes us strong.

It would be kind of cool to come back as a human, I must admit, but based on what I witnessed in her life it is not a life I am eager to live.

But it's food for thought.

Curve Ball

Just when I thought she was getting on track with her new life, we were both thrown a curve ball.

I've mentioned Grandfather Tree, the mulberry tree in our little park before. She would always go there when her heart was troubled, so needless to say she went there quite often in the days following my departure. This particular day she was sitting at the base of the tree dissecting her relationship with Benjamin. They had been dating for several months and she had a choice to make. He was being promoted to a national firm and was moving to San Francisco. He had asked her to join him.

She really liked him and she felt the adventure could be exciting. As she sat there beneath the huge heart-shaped leaves, the answer came to her. No. She could not go. Grandfather Tree always gave her the right answers.

She came to realize that she had very different values and goals than Benjamin. He was climbing the corporate ladder and his goal was to be rich, have a big house and a fancy car. It's why he was taking the promotion...to work harder to make more money to live the kind of life he wanted to live. Kate had become very sick in the process of working to pay for the house that we ended up losing anyway. When she was given a second chance at health and was well again, she made the decision that she no longer wanted to work such long hours to pay for a life she couldn't live because she was working such long hours.

She was downsizing. Simplifying. While she was trying to stretch her faith and quiet her mind, Benjamin was trying to stretch his wallet and his resume. It seemed that remaining with Benjamin would take her further away from her priorities.

I was glad that he was moving and that she was deciding to stay right where she was, for another better plan. Another better man.

As she sat there under our tree, she remembered the moments that had become priceless. She thought of the feel of my fur, of my paw. The way I would look at her from under my shaggy bangs. The way we felt, the love we shared. I began to miss those things as she was missing them.

You think the things you can touch and feel are the things that are real, but they are not. Over time, they all get old and decline. The people, the houses, the rocks and the mountains: one day they will all crumble. This is because they are not as real as the things that last forever. It is another one of the lessons we come to teach.

Desire Draws Us Forward

When we live upon the earth, we need our physical bodies to touch, smell, and taste physical things. When we make the transition into Heaven we no longer need our bodies. There is nothing we need them for. We shed them like a second skin.

I took some time to pause and look back at the life I shared with her. I remembered the feeling of my head in her lap and how she held me, her hands and heart heavy with love for me. How we ran through the garden together, the wind in our hair. The scents and sights of the ever-changing seasons. Cheese and peanut butter on my tongue! The smell of bacon in the fry pan. A long cold drink after a long hot day. Most of all, I remembered the way she loved me. I remembered the day I realized that it was because of me that she had learned to love. I found myself wanting to feel that way again. I wanted to feel her and kiss her face once again.

I took a snooze. I had a dream. I dreamed of my favorite yummy salmon skin treats.

It is the desire for material things of the earth, the things that delight the senses, that is the magnet that draws us back. Some of us are above and beyond all earthly desires having lived so many lifetimes that all we need is to be joined with God and Spirit. When we are completely fulfilled, we want for nothing else.

For the majority of us who still feel the need for love and attachment to people, places and things, we will keep returning. I was finding that I still had earthly desires and I was then thinking of going back. I loved her so much that I could not fathom coming back as anything but a dog. Her dog.

It had been a divine set up. My Master sent me to her to teach her how wonderful it is to love and be loved so that when I was gone from her she would yearn for love again. She would no longer be afraid of love. Soon she would one day realize that the love we shared was her reward for taking a chance on love, for taking a chance on me. Oh if her fear had gotten in the way, what we both would have missed!

She was still alone. She had Immy and Joey, but it just wasn't enough. She needed human love too. By having me in her life she had come to believe that she did not need any other kind of companion.

Many evenings we would sit on the front porch and watch the sun go down. "How does it get any better than this?" she would say to me, her bare foot resting lightly on my back. "Why would I ever want anything else?"

She would stay at home with me rather than go out on the town with her friends. She chose to travel with me rather than take vacations with family. I had, so far, been the love of her life. She made me her everything. She didn't realize then that when you make someone your everything, when they are gone you have nothing left.

I have since learned that our Master sends us soul mates who teach us to depend on them and then we come to believe we cannot live without them. Then He takes them away to prove to us that we can indeed live without them, but also to prove that we cannot live without Him.

Planning My Return

It was time. He was standing before me awaiting my decision. My Master had heard the desires of my heart and He had been very clear with me. I trust everything He has ever said to me. He told me that I would not be sent back to her because she already learned what I went there to teach her the first time around. He assured me that I would be sent to a different home, but that it would be a home filled with love. I would be a different breed and a different sex. We all come back in a new way, a new costume, so that we can learn new lessons, teach new lessons and acquire new experience. It was yet another gift He was offering to me.

The bottom line for me was that I could wait passively at Home for her until she returns, like I always did, or I could make the most of the time between now and then by living a new kind of life. Heaven is in the Rainbow Time Zone where time does not exist. My Master reminded me that time is an illusion and that, by design, it would be synchronized so that I would be there waiting for her at the edge of the Bridge on the day that she was scheduled to arrive. He promised me that it would work out perfectly. Things would happen in her life and in mine so that everything takes place at the right time in the right place although not necessarily in what would seem to be the right way. After all, sometimes a tragedy must happen to keep a soul on schedule. This is the reason for things that seem to have no reason. This is the reason that we cannot fathom when we are going through it.

Perhaps I will get very sick. People wonder why cancer exists when it is just a clever method to teach people lessons about love and loss. It borrows time or steals it depending on the needs of Heaven. It is a vehicle to get us where we need to be. It calls us home because something needs us there.

We always leave the earth for a very good reason. I might be hit by a car and it would all seem such a tragedy to those who love me upon the earth, but it would be the way I could return to Rainbow Bridge so that I could be there at the right moment in time to greet her as she comes across.

I decided that I wasn't quite ready. I could not go back there into a different kind of life knowing that deep in my heart and soul I would worry about her. After all, I've been watching her much like a human watches a favorite TV show. The one watching can get all caught up in it and then they don't want to stop watching it until it's over.

There was still one thing I needed to do. A match I needed to make...

Soul Mates

Hmmm. Salt and Pepper. In the quiet times, she would wonder who he was. His name. Where he lived. If he loved. If he could love her. So much time had passed.

I had been trying to make a meeting happen between them but no matter how hard you try, nothing can happen until the time is right.

One day she pulled in beside him at the post office and I saw her see him there. She was arriving and he was leaving. He never saw her. It's like the man zigs while she zags. If she was to meet him, it was not the right time.

As the days passed, she kept crossing paths with him. Most of the time she didn't see him because her mind was on other things. He didn't see her because his mind was on other things.

When she was hiking the trail, he was biking the trail. Beyond his helmet, sunglasses and bike, she didn't recognize him. He didn't recognize her because he was still too stressed to pay much attention to anything outside of his thoughts. He would ride his mountain bike very fast and precariously. Whatever he needed to do. It was a unique way to live in the moment.

Taking risks often can help one to keep one's mind off of one's troubles.

A few minutes before arriving in a parking lot, she would always ask the angels to give her a safe parking spot in one of her favorite places. This particular day as she approached "her" spot, a fancy car slipped quickly into it. She grumbled to think that the Universe had let her down as she drove over to the other side of the lot and parked her car there.

The Universe didn't let her down at all. The angels were arranging an important meeting between two old friends in her favorite spot, so that's why they couldn't give it to her. They were also arranging something in the spot she had just pulled into.

I looked at the car next to us and it was him! Salt and Pepper. She saw him there too and was caught off guard. Glancing in the mirror, she quickly fixed her hair and put a dab of lipstick on her lips and on her cheeks, but he had already gone into the store.

I was so glad that I could walk with her behind the veil now. It has its benefits. Where once I would have had to wait in the car for her to come out, I could now go right into the grocery store with her and witness it all unfold! She quickly grabbed a cart and headed over to the aisle full of veggies and fruits. She would always start on the right hand side of the store and work her way to the left. He would start on the left hand side and work towards the right. Somehow this day they missed each other in the center aisles. I don't know how that happened. But wait, she forgot to get the avocados! She headed back over to the vegetable aisle and there he was, at the avocados.

Ha-ha!

As she arrived he looked up at her.

"Hi."

"Oh... Hi."

It was so funny. They had the same stuff in their grocery carts. Almond milk, cottage cheese, cage free eggs, pasta, veggies and fruits. Now avocados.

"Do I know you?" he asked her.

"I don't know you but I remember you," she said, trying to be nonchalant even though her heart was in her throat and she felt her cheeks getting hot.

"I'm sorry, I can hardly recall," he said, "but I do. I do remember you. My name is Luke." He extended his hand.

"Hi Luke, I'm Kate," she replied as she shook his hand warmly.

He looked at her as if to say something but then thought better of it.

"Well," he said, putting the chosen avocado in his cart, "It was nice to see you again." She saw that he still wore a ring on his left hand. He was gone before she could respond and he left her looking after him as he hurried away.

"I will never understand men," she said under her breath.

You understood me, I said to her. *You'll understand him too and someday you'll understand what you don't understand now.*

I began to notice what love does. Salt and Pepper inspired her to think about things long forgotten. She would be ready next time. She went into her closet one day and pulled out her most feminine clothes. Most of them were hanging far at the back of the closet. She started getting her hair done more often and she updated her eyeglasses. She hadn't cared in a very long time but love makes us care again. Love pulls us forward. Love reminds us that we're worth it. That's what love does.

I liked calling him Salt and Pepper but she liked to say his name out loud.

"Luke," she would say, dreamily. Even though the higher soul was working overtime, she was thinking that for something happen, she had to be the one to Make It Happen. She didn't know that we all knew the desires of her heart and that we were banding together for her highest good to help her obtain them.

She even changed her route to work thinking she might cross paths with him. The funny thing is that by changing her routine to suit her search, she was altering the course and actually making it harder for us to arrange a meeting.

Soul Families

Some of us have deeper feelings for one over another. It can't be helped. It's chemistry. It's inherent. You can't make yourself love someone you don't and you can't make yourself stop loving someone you do.

We each get glimmers of true love throughout our life. Little fragments, feelings, starlit experiences touched by the spirit of our collective souls. The moments are often fleeting as they guide us to the one who is meant to be with us...the one we gave our heart to many moons ago in a life long before this one.

This is why some people keep searching even though they have something quite nice walking right beside them. We all make the most of the relationships that we have until one day we are reunited with our truest loves.

It does not always happen in this lifetime. Some of us take many lifetimes. The more we love the more loves we are able to have. The more mature we are the more souls are right for us. Some day when we all ripen in our love and our ability to love and be loved, everyone will be our soul mate. In the meantime we make the best of things.

Kate would often look wistfully at Immy. Was she happy? Did she wish she were back in Montana again? When she runs, what is she running from? What is she running to? Meanwhile Joey would never leave her side. He loved Kate relentlessly.

"Immy," she said, "you are a stranger to me. I've had you for quite some time, yet you are not mine. Your heart is somewhere else."

She was right. A piece of Immy's heart was somewhere else with someone else; someone she committed to long, long ago. A piece of Kate's heart was somewhere else too. The right loved one will fill up your life like the final puzzle piece that makes it all complete. You feel it when you meet them. Or sometimes if you aren't mature enough or wise enough, it can take time to discover that they are the right one. Once your jigsaw puzzle is complete, the rest are often just extra pieces.

The truth is that while Immy loved Kate dearly, there was another she loved more. Just like I was waiting at Rainbow Bridge for Kate to return to me, Immy had a loved one there too. One that surpassed all others.

Soul mates. How else can you explain loving someone who never gave you cause to love? How do you feel you know someone even though you never met them before?

Time Reveals the Truth

Immy was adjusting slowly. I watched them all night one night when Immy was sound asleep lying across the corner of the bed on my quilt. When she first got onto the bed, she had taken Kate's place so that there was no room left for Kate.

"No way," Kate said to her sternly, "That's my place. Find another place for yourself." She went into the bathroom to brush her teeth and when she later returned to the bed, Immy had moved and she never ever took Kate's place again.

When Immy first came home she used Joey as her guide. She copied everything he did. She did not know how to be a pet. Having lived in a kennel her first two years on earth, she did not know how to be part of a family. She did not know how to be a "dog". When Joey jumped with joy when Kate came home from work, Immy would jump around and make little squealing noises too. When Joey raced out the front door like a racehorse out of a gate, Immy raced out there too. We all need a role model. I was Joey's and Joey was Immy's.

Kate would often gaze upon them and pensively remember how easy I had been to live with. Immy did not easily allow herself to be loved. She acted aloof and nonchalant. When people came over to visit, Joey would clamor all over them with his love. If they were lucky, Immy would come say a quick hello and then go off to do her own thing. She never had much use for most people, preferring to retreat to her own quiet safe space. Kate would sometimes roll her eyes in a humorous way when she spoke of Immy but you can't see something in someone else unless you possess those qualities yourself.

Immy would never look Kate in the eye. Everyone said, "It's the breed. They're aloof." But it was more than that. Kate knew it was more than that. Immy was very sensitive to the tone of her voice and the energy of her being. That energy came out of her hands this particular morning when Immy came to her for some attention. Kate took Immy's long face in her hands.

"No matter how much they directed you to perform, groomed you to make you "perfect", no matter how many times you failed, you are still beautiful. You are still smart! You are capable! You are... love... and that is all that matters."

In a flash of insight, she took a deep breath.
"Oh my goodness, look what's happening," she stated. "I give you what I myself have needed. We need each other. I need you too."

Immy was getting better all the time. So was Kate. It would be a matter of time but the day would come when they would both learn that they are accepted and loved without condition. They will then offer total love in return because when the fear is gone and we finally trust that we are safe, love is able to step into the space that fear left behind.

Meanwhile Joey kept climbing all over them like a lunatic. He was saying, "I can help! I can teach you! Let me teach you to be like me!" For Joey lived in the bliss of unconditional love all the time. He would carry them the rest of the way.

Anniversaries of the Heart

The first of every month loomed ominously. The August 1 anniversary was especially tough. She had made it through one year of loss; cycled through every anniversary of the heart; 365 "firsts" without me. Oh, but it was still complicated, leaving that first year behind. It's like she lost that too.

Then a funny thing happened. December 1 arrived. Sixteen months. The day came and went. On December 2 she realized she had not noticed it. She felt guilty at first until she realized, with my help, that it was cause for celebration! It was a sign of her healing. My life was the important thing and our relationship, now on new terms, was all that mattered. She forgot February 1 too! And March! She didn't remember until after a whole week had passed! Who knew what would happen on April Fool's Day? Well! She fooled me and remembered! This is how it will happen for you too -- in your own time and in your own way.

She asked me, 'How can so much time have passed and yet it seems like yesterday?' Because time doesn't really exist. Meanwhile man does his very best to try to control everything. It's man who created sundials, clocks and calendars thinking somehow he could control time. Everything that ever happened, happened just a moment ago. Everything ahead will take place in the blink of an eye.

Have you ever walked along a beach? You walk towards something in the distance. For the longest while it never seems to get any closer even though you are walking and walking. Then all of a sudden, you are there. You've arrived at last. That's what grief is like. Meanwhile we are running with you in the spray of the surf at the edge of the shore where the sand meets the sea. We are cheering you on.

Blind Date

It was a cold and blustery night. She was driving up the interstate to meet up with a guy on a blind date. He lived in the next town an hour away. I already knew it wasn't the right guy because the right guy would not have had her drive all that way. He would have gone to her instead.

She had written his phone number and the address of the location of the park where they were to meet before going to dinner and a movie. The paper she wrote it on was tucked in the space above the visor on the driver's side.

I watched it all unfold. She had the car window open for fresh air, as she usually does, with the heater blasting. The further up the highway she went, the darker and windier it got. She didn't close her window, oh no! The wind tossed her car about on the road. Then! A huge gust seemed to come right in through her window, lift the visor and out blew the piece of paper with the guy's phone number and the address...sixty-five miles per hour out into the night.

She tried to meet him anyway, going on memory. She went to every park that she could find but alas, he was nowhere to be found.

Upon arriving home much later, he had left her a voicemail message. He was angry with her for standing him up and he didn't want to speak to her ever again. This is how she knew he was not The One. If she'd hooked up with him, it would have taken her a very long time to find out how critical and unforgiving he was. It would have taken her too long to find out that he was not the right man for her. It would have interfered with a better plan written just for her.

Our Master can see it all. If you drive down a long curvy road, you don't see the twists and turns until you are on top of them. But when you see things from a much higher perspective, you can see the whole road and the twists and the turns and the beginning and the end. In Heaven we can see where you are in relation to where you're going and we can make things happen along the way at the intersections of life. We can create the right time and the right place and we can already see how it all ends. We can see the whole story of your life while you are living it in little bits and pieces.

When you schedule a date you can show up at the right time but be in the wrong place or be in the right place at the wrong time. You need both the right time and the right place to make something happen. Our Master is the one who sets the date and your heart is the one who answers the call.

Where Love Lived

I loved fortune cookies. She'd give me the cookies and then would read the fortunes that were tucked inside of them. One night she opened one up and it said, "Whether your luck is good or whether it's bad, one thing is for sure. It will change."

Sooner or later in life, change is inevitable. She would try to cling to the good times and suffer through the bad times. They ebbed and flowed, for that is how life is. She had a tendency to change her life on a fairly regular basis. Every few years she would seek a new relationship, find a new job or move into a new house. In her heart she felt that if she were complacent for too long, God would create circumstances that would force her to change. She wanted to beat Him to the punch.

The day came when she made the choice to vacate the house we last shared. It was the home that lay at the base of my trail where we lived and where we loved and where I "died".

The move was difficult for her. For all I had taught her, she still felt she was leaving me behind at the house and on the trail. She seemed to forget that the moment I left her side I flew straight into her heart and planted a seed of love that would grow and spread far and wide.

It was her last night in the house. She had worked many weeks sorting and packing. She had a lot of boxes filled with donations for the local thrift shop. As she went through her files, she found my old vet bills...and filed them back into the files. She uncovered the raised double dog dish that Grady and I had eaten from. She had hidden it from herself so that she wouldn't feel bad when she saw it. Now she was finding everything. There was no escape. She thought of donating it too, but breathed a deep sigh of relief when her good friends were happy to take it. She found my old pain meds far at the back inside the refrigerator. I was glad that she threw them away. I wish she had done it way back then, but people will do what people will do.

A small bottle of champagne was still in the fridge. She wanted to take it up to our trail by the creek bed, sit beside "me" and drink to celebrate me. The bubbly was chilling in the fridge but she lost track of time and was racing the clock to be out of the house by midnight because the lease told her that she must leave by then.

After deciding she was simply too tired to enjoy the champagne, she packed it into the final box, which she placed in the backseat of her car. She would find a better time and place to celebrate. She then walked room to room to say goodbye to the house.

She started at the place of my "death" on the kitchen floor by the door to the pantry. She began to cry as she often would when she thought of us lying there in my final and difficult hours. Then she shook it off. She knew that it would make me unhappy to have her cry at my expense. She leaned tiredly against the pantry door.

"Thank you Jack," she said to me. "Thank you for allowing me to be with you through each and every moment."

It was in those hours on the kitchen floor that she had begun to truly learn the art of being Present. She watched me breathe. She felt my fur. She lay beside me, her heart to my heart. It is one of the gifts of death and loss, to teach how to focus and live in the present moment.

As she stood at the pantry, I covered her with my goose bumps. She had learned to recognize me when I came to her this way. We stayed there together, my energy mingled with hers, and gradually her lips curved into a gentle smile. While she was smiling, bright tears of devotion fell from her eyes. They were not tears of sadness or regret. They were tears that fell because she knew she had been blessed by my love and had been gifted with my life.

Just before she shut off the light in the kitchen for the last time, she made a pact with me. "When I close this light, I close the door to that bitter memory of you in your final hour. I will only remember the good times. I know it's up to me to stay in a peaceful place and control my tears and discipline my mind so that my unhappiness does not make you unhappy too."

She had learned. We are connected at the heart and her state of mind affects my state of being. We can never be separated and we need to be guardians of one another's peace and happiness.

She turned off the kitchen light and walked through the rest of the house. So many memories were there, mostly happy ones and some were sad. She let go of the sad ones as they came to her. She remembered how I struggled to hoist myself off the ceramic tile floor in the foyer by the front door and she knew she'd never wish me back.

As she locked the front door for the last time, leaving the house in total darkness, she stopped for one more memory. The wall. The lizard. The Lizard from Rainbow Bridge. The messenger who came to escort me to my heavenly home. Lizard was the unexpected angel who made sure that she finished my first book and began a journey to fulfill her destiny in a way she never expected.

As she walked pensively to the overflowing car at the curb, she realized what had taken place in her life, in her heart. The grief, which had once been so unbearable, had been replaced with a fascination with signs and messengers. She had begun to notice the great synchronicity of the universe. Lizards and butterflies.

Clouds and dreams. Things that come in metaphors that speak the language of the heart. Her amazement as she searched and found the gifts that came from the loss of me became stronger than her grief. It pulled her forward, kept her aware of the ever-changing magic around her and deepened her faith in a Master in Heaven who oversees all of us no matter how small.

As she got into the car she looked back towards the house and in an uncertain moment she paused.

"C'mon Jack! Come with me."

Then she whistled, the whistle that always brought me running. I went with her, of course I did. I've never left her side. Nothing can separate two who have been joined by our heavenly Master. Not angels. Not demons. Not grief.

Heaven is Here

We all live in the same space. I know it's hard to believe if you've been taught that Heaven is up in the sky somewhere beyond the clouds.

Heaven is all around you. You just can't see us because we are vibrating at a higher level than you are. It's kind of like a dog whistle. There is a noise, a pitch so high that the human ear cannot detect it but it is there nonetheless, for don't you see all the dogs come running!

When we cross Rainbow Bridge we become only love and love is the highest level of vibration; the highest "pitch" so to speak. This is why you cannot see us. We are here, only gone from your sight until one day you are the same vibration as we are. When you vibrate in love all the time you will not have to ask again if I am here, you will know that I am here with you.

There is no "other" place. There is only one, this one. I'm not somewhere out beyond the stars! Do you think that Heaven's far from Earth? It is not far. They are the same! The place doesn't change; it's we who do. The body that you think is "you", isn't you at all. It just contains and separates you from the Heaven that surrounds. One day you will leave it too, just the way that I left mine. You'll be surprised but you will find the moment when you shed your skin, we'll be together again. (Jack McAfghan: Book 1, Chapter 85)

Interconnected

I was sure that she would feel the shift when I made the transition from Heaven to Earth. She would know in her heart that something had happened. She would feel my absence because a part of me would be somewhere else. I could see it all unfold. She would say "Jack, where are you? I don't feel you here anymore." She would think I had forsaken her.

I thought about coming to her in a dream and telling her that I would be coming back to the earth plane, just so she wouldn't worry about where I was, but then I quickly changed my mind. I knew that if I told her this it would delay her course. It would take over. I knew everything about her. I knew that she would rise to the challenge and never let go. Driven by her love and longing for me, she would only look frantically around to try to find me. She would wonder for the rest of her life where I am, where I was, if I'd come, if I'd gone. Till the end of time she would wonder about me. How on earth would she find me? How would she possibly know which one was me? She could end up with dozens of dogs and none of them would be me.

How did she know the first time around? How did I? Because it was our destiny. I thought about how it might change her destiny, her looking for me, and how that might change the Grand Plan. It could ruin everything. I cannot tell her. It is not the loving thing to do. I must bear this journey without her.

It was a big decision for me because I was going into it knowing full well what would happen. When and if we are born again, the memory of our previous lifetimes is fully erased from our memory for if it wasn't, we would spend all our time on earth trying to find those things, those loves, those attachments we had in previous lifetimes. I would spend all my time looking for her just like I imagined she would look for me. It would defeat the purpose of living the next lifetime for we would all forever be chasing those we felt attached to at the risk of not living the new life we've been given. It would be like going back to a school you already graduated from or wearing shoes that are too small. It would be like going to a party and sitting comfortably at a table with your closest friends, never expanding your circle to include others who might be well worth knowing.

My Master told me not to worry. He would see to it that I have everything I need. He would see that she had everything she needed too. All I needed to do was to keep my faith in Him and trust my journey.

She was finally done with her grief. The moment she fully let me go was the moment I could return to her world.

It was time for me to make my passage.

Humanimals

2 cells turn into 4 turn into 8 turn into 16 turn into 32 turn into 64. The building blocks of everything come together in the 64 cells that create a puppy. 64 cells filled with DNA. DNA filled with the deeply stored memory of all the lives we've ever lived.

Some say we are not like humans but we are more like them than we are different. Man and animals are in the same species as mammals as they have mammary glands that produce the milk to nurse their young. Their lungs breathe air and their blood is warm. They are vertebrates in that their skeletal system and well-designed spines hold their bodies together. Each cell is made of molecules, each molecule is made of atoms, and each atom is made of protons, neutrons and mostly electrons, which are made of waves of fibered light.

Earth scientists are just now studying this, but those fibered waves of light come from where we come from. We are more spirit than we are anything else. All of us. Man and animal. We are all the same, just off by a teeny tiny chromosome or two.

I was ready. The decision had been made. The genetic process had taken place and it was time for me to go. There was a tiny body waiting for me to bring life into it. My spirit prepared itself to live in a new kind of body and a new kind of world. I had been told that the memory of being here would be erased. The moment I was told this I made a point of trying to remember everything.

I was reminded just before I left, that I would be loved. I have apparently earned great love from all the lifetimes I have lived giving all the love I have to give. It's true. Sooner or later we always get what we give.

Rebirth

Animals don't really put a lot of thought into having babies. Our Master puts the desire to procreate in us to be sure that we are fruitful and multiply. He knows how important animals are to the planet because most animals He allows to reproduce in great number. He put every one of us on the ark for a reason.

Do you think it's a mistake that dogs and cats have litters of 8, 9, 10 or more and people typically only have one or maybe two? It's no mistake. It's because God intends that there is more than enough four-legged love to go around. The problems come when humans start getting careless or greedy and they start breeding for money or by accident and then society ends up with more animals than it can handle.

The environment our mother lives in during her pregnancy impacts the energy of the pups. Were we bred by parents genetically chosen for health and beauty? Was our mother overbred by a relentless backyard breeder? Perhaps we were born into a puppy mill like I was the last time, or maybe the first home we had was a garbage dump or alley. Whatever the circumstance, we accept our life for what it is and we always strive to love the one who is our keeper. If there is toil and strife, poverty and sickness, we will feel that when we arrive. If we are born into an atmosphere of love and appreciation, we will feel that. It creates the foundation from which we live the rest of our lives upon the earth.

In human births it's important too. The moment of birth can shape a human more than any other event. The state of consciousness when you are conceived can impact your development too. Were you born out of a loving union or were you born out of physical need? Was your conception an act of love or did it take place in an environment of pain, violence or desperation? All will have their impact.

Just as the first moments of life can impact the quality of the life to come, the moments preceding one's death can also impact the life to come. A peaceful passing is the secret to a peaceful journey over the rainbow. We take that peace with us and we take the love with us and we run unencumbered by anything else. Nothing else matters.

Death gets a bad rap. People think that euthanasia is putting their pets "down" when it really is lifting us up. In the first moment, when we come back to earth, we remember the comfort of the Heaven we came from and this is why we cry when we are born. When we are born in Heaven we come in laughing not crying! In birth we have the passage and then the pain. In death we have the pain and then the passage.

Culture Shock

I was back on earth. I was a puppy again. I was brown and smooth coated this time. One of several girls and several boys, I was not big I was not small. I needed to learn to walk again. And smell and see and eat and pee. And feel. And love.

I needed help learning how to live this kind of life again. I would need to be nurtured by my mother. I would also need to be held and cared for by human hands. A living being needs these things as it grows, to thrive.

I once met a rabbit at Rainbow Bridge whose earthly fate was to be a part of a laboratory experiment. He had never received love. He had never been touched. How could it be that he had been brought into that kind of life, when his fur was so soft that it would heal the one touching it? There are many who live without love. There were many at Rainbow Bridge who never knew love and they had all died young or spent a lifetime failing to thrive.

I took my first breath. In that breath was a unique imprint of universal energy. Based on the planets and the stars and calendars and the seasons, it would give me a certain genetic makeup. Some people call it astrology. Others call it "design". It would give me certain characteristics that were uniquely mine and would come be an inherent part of who I would become.

I was feeling bewildered. My brain wasn't formed yet so I couldn't really focus on much of anything.

We take our first breath and then we think our first thought. The last thought we had as we left our previous life becomes the first thought we have in the next. Like a movie sequel that picks up right where it left off, the final thought in our last life sets the stage when we come back. That's why it's so important to be at peace at the end of that life. Because life goes on.

I remembered the thought. The last one in that life. I could hear the words ringing in the echoes of my being. "I love you, Jack. I love you. Run free little boy. Go Home. Run free," she was saying to me.

All of a sudden an image of her came shining through. I saw myself reflected in her eyes. I remembered that I loved her beyond love and that I would never ever forget her. I knew in my heart and soul that I would one day be reunited with her. In the very moment as I was thinking that thought, it was leaving me. It happened so fast, in a millisecond.

My mind once again became a clear slate, but my head was foggy. My brain was not developed yet. Nothing was really. I was not thinking about anything. I couldn't see anything. I couldn't make sense of anything. My heart though, my heart remembered. It remembered love. It remembered the choice I was given to come here again. Somewhere deep within me like a bunch of dreams I couldn't quite remember, was the remembrance of every life I'd ever lived. I especially remembered the one I shared with her because my life with her was my very favorite one.

At the moment of my birth I knew all this information, information that slipped away from me even as I slipped from the warm softness that was my mother, onto the cold hard floor. I had to forget my heart for a while to let my brain take shape.

It was uncomfortable for me. I felt incredibly ill at ease after the delight of Heaven and the warm protection of my mother's womb. Something weighed heavy upon me. I sensed that others like me were there too, all around me and on top of me. I could not see them, I could not hear. I could only feel the strange world that I had been born into.

I was cold and wet. I sought comfort. I began to get upset and found myself uttering tiny whimpers and whines. My mother started licking me, grooming me. Well, I didn't know it was my mother then, but it was a stable loving presence that had been designed to take care of me. In that moment I learned my first lesson: When you whimper, someone will respond. The one who responds is the one you learn to depend upon. I knew I belonged to her. My mother. All I wanted was her. I kept seeking her out until I found her and the sweet warmth of her milk. I learned that I had to share her with the others. This would not be the first or the last time I would want someone all to myself. We all come yearning for love and attention. We tend to transfer the love we have felt for our loving Master in Heaven to any loving substitute while we live upon the earth.

Soon, human hands lifted me out of the box to hold me and to pet me. I quickly came to understand that humans are not to be feared and that they will care for me too. It was all about me although I didn't really know what I was. I breathed. I felt. I didn't really think about anything. I didn't know much of anything. I only knew my life was new. I lived my life as if it revolved around me. I knew my heart was strong. I knew my Master was watching over me.

I slept. I dreamed.

My World Opens Up

It was so strange, like waking up from a deep sleep. I had done it a hundred or maybe a thousand times before. For a brief moment I had to ask myself where I was, here or there or the other place. The last time I remembered waking up like this I found myself at Wild Horse Mesa just before crossing Rainbow Bridge.

I was not sure who or what I was or where. I just knew that I had been somehow reborn into the light of a new day.

My very first experience of pain came from my very own mother biting me! She nipped me when I pushed the limits, but by doing so she was teaching me how to use my own teeth to communicate without hurting someone. Is it play or is it aggression? When you play, you use your teeth to tease. When you are aggressive, you bite to hurt in order to protect yourself or someone else. My mother was so wise! She taught me by her example how far I could go. I learned to control my bite to fit the circumstance.

My senses started coming alive. My nose picked up on all kinds of smells and my quiet world started opening up. Light came into my eyes and sounds entered my ears. I learned to use my mouth for food but I also came to realize that sometimes sounds would come out of my mouth too.

I came to learn that one of my sisters was stillborn. When we prepare to come back into an earth body, sometimes we change our mind at the last minute. It can cause a lot of drama on this end. I'm glad I didn't change my mind. I was learning so much here, more than I ever would have learned in Heaven where I came from, for we know everything there and there is nothing new under the sun. Heaven is perfect and one can only learn through experience and adversity.

There was a commotion. I could feel the emotions of the people in the barn. The breeder man was talking with a lady who had come to see the pups. He said, "We take great care of our pups and extra care right now because if anything were to happen to upset one of them, it could remain an issue for them for the rest of its natural born life."

The breeder man was making sure that our family would be well cared for. The breeder man reminded me of my Master in Heaven. I could still remember Him. It seemed just a moment ago. I thought about her again, but I could not tune into her as easily as I did when I didn't have so much going on around me.

Sensing the Shift

She was watching for me. Just like I thought she would. She sensed that there had been a shift but she didn't understand it. She looked for clouds and feathers. She would reach out but not find.

"Jack are you there? Where did you go? I don't feel you anymore." "Jack where are you?" "Did you leave me?"

Her head was bothered but she knew in her heart exactly what was going on. One day she got so obsessed with the thought that I was no longer in Heaven and had come back as a pup, that she went online and looked at all the dogs she could find that were born after the day of my departure. I knew I had to nip this behavior in the bud. This behavior was not part of the plan. She needed relief.

That night I asked my soul to go to her soul to let her know that I still loved her. To tell her not to look for me. To let her know that I was just a little preoccupied doing some other things for a while, but to reassure her that I still loved her most of all.

Later that night, before she went to sleep, she called for me. "Dear Jack – Please come. I want to dream of you." She laid her head on the pillow and placed her hands on her heart, breathed and believed. Together we entered the Land of Dreams. I was determined to reach her. I knew I would find a way to let her know what was going on with me.

We dreamed. I showed myself to her. We were riding in the car. I was in the passenger seat. I knew this would get her attention because I never liked riding in the passenger seat; I always rode in the back seat. When she let me out of the car, I ran happily all around! I wanted to show her beyond a doubt how happy I was because I knew that this would make her happy too. When I left the car I looked just like I did when I was hers. When I turned back to look at her after I ran around the farmhouse, I had turned myself into a Chocolate Lab. I looked right into her eyes and she looked right into mine. My eyes were the same eyes I had before; it was just my body that was different. I told her clearly not to be looking for me for I still lived inside her heart. I told her everything was okay. I told her in the dream that I wanted her to remember this because it was very important.

She woke up and she remembered. She wrote it down in her dream journal so she would be sure not to forget. She hoped that someday it might make sense looking back on it.

Growing Pains

I was really clumsy. We all seemed to be climbing all over and falling on top of each other. We were all learning to walk. So many things were happening. I was getting old enough to observe what was going on around me. There was another group of puppies in a box nearby. The breeder man took a lot of time over there. The mother died during the birth and he was working very closely with them for the pups had to learn to live with abandonment and other emotional issues as a result. We are a lot like people. Whatever happens to us in the very early years can impact us the rest of our lives.

We were getting bigger. We were realizing that we were living breathing beings, not the angels we were before we came here. It was very humbling. Some of us remembered this and others would never even think about it. Some dogs, people and other animals too, forget that they are spiritual beings playing out a role on earth in a unique body that they were given as a costume to wear at the masquerade of life.

I was fully aware of my body and it was soft and furry and brown. It felt kind of strange for the last I knew I was blonde with long hair, but it was the beginning of a wonderful new adventure.

We began exploring outside our mother's bed box. I went to look at the other puppy box and they looked very different from my family. Two were sleeping all the time instead of exploring. Three of them were whimpering. I somehow knew that the litter needed special attention. They didn't have much energy. Two of them had died inside their mother. It seemed quite sad but I knew that it was because their souls were needed somewhere else.

For just a moment I remembered Heaven. Like a fleeting dream, I made a point of trying to remember it because I knew it was important and would be something that would inspire me as I moved forward into the earthly world. I would need it. I would need to find a way to stay connected to it no matter what happens here.

Little by little I felt my world expand. Life is kind of like a goldfish in a tank. If a fish tank holds a gallon of water, the fish will grow to fill the gallon. If the tank holds ten gallons, the same fish will grow to the size of ten gallons. Such is life. As your life expands, you grow in your wisdom and experience to fill it. The only limits on life are those that you yourself put on it.

I found myself willing to take a few steps away from the security of my mother. The breeder man seemed to be drawing us further and further from the whelping box. He knew that to have healthy happy dogs that we would need to be socialized. We would know nothing of the world if we never left the box we were born in. We needed to let go of our dependency on our mother and to ultimately learn to depend on a human parent. He knew we needed to be comfortable in the presence of other kinds of dogs and animals. And people. I knew that I would be okay. I had confidence in the man and I knew that he was doing his very best for us. I also had faith that my Master was always watching, making sure I would be okay.

Feeding time! We all scurried over to the dish and I could see the personalities of my brothers and sisters taking shape. The big boy was a shrinking violet and the big girl seemed to be boss. Sometimes the breeder man would come and separate her from the rest of us so she wouldn't keep scaring and intimidating the others. He needed us to be in perfect condition because he was getting ready sell us to our new families.

You may wonder how we "decide" whether we want to be boss or not, but did you decide how you wanted your personality to be? Probably not because it is an imprint you bring with you when you decide to come back into this life. I had been alpha and I had been shrinking violet but because I learned by living those lives that I would rather be moderate and happy, I learned that I wanted to stay right in the middle. I have asked for nothing. It was always my favorite way to be. When I looked around, I was glad that I was me. I was also glad that I was born into this family. They have helped me to see who I am and they have taught me how to interact with others. Many people and animals never receive this kind of training.

Easing Into Life

The breeder man was very kind. I liked him a lot. He would sit down and talk to us and tell us what to expect from the life we were living with him. I wanted to stay here with him forever! He taught us about toys and gave us a tour of the big yard outdoors. I couldn't believe it when I saw that there was a whole big world right outside our birthing room! He was preparing us for a big change and he wanted us to be ready for it. He knew how hard it was for us to understand the human ways and he laughed about that. He said that it would take the rest of our lives on earth to understand fully what life is all about. I wanted to understand right there and then what he meant but I believed him and I figured that I would know soon enough.

It was so wonderful when we went out onto the grass outside! It was so cool and lush and for a moment I remembered the green fields of Heaven with the little yellow flowers. Just as I was beginning to remember the Rainbow Forest, the breeder man's kids came over and we got to play with them. There were other dogs too. And cats! It was fun! The breeder man lifted me up and looked me in my eyes and told me that I was his favorite. I think he was saying that to each one of us. I think it was his final gift to help each one of us know that we were special.

One day a lady came to visit us and she wanted to take two of my sisters home with her, right then and there. She got mad at the breeder man because he would not let her take them so young.

"I want them. I've got good money to pay for them," she said in a huff, "I can pay you in cash."

"You don't understand, lady," he replied, "These pups need more time with their mother to develop. They still need to learn about bonding and about being part of a family. It isn't all about you and your money."

When she finally left, he wiped his brow and heaved a sigh of relief. Even I was glad that she was gone. She had changed the energy of our place while she was here. The breeder man explained to all of us that our brains were not yet capable of understanding many things. He told us not to feel bad about it; it's just the way it is.

One morning I went over to see my mother for breakfast and I was very surprised when she pushed me away. I kind of took it personally until I saw that she was pushing all of us away. She was even nipping at some of the others. I guessed she was tired of feeding us. I missed her milk, but the breeder man brought us food, different kinds of food, to sustain us. It was all very interesting because my mouth hurt from all the little pointy things growing in there. I didn't understand it but the day I tasted kibble for the first time, I realized that I needed the pointy things to eat it. I started looking to the breeder man for my food instead of to my mother. She was not around so much anymore. I was not quite sure to whom I belonged.

I was so glad that I never forgot my Master in Heaven. I knew I belonged to Him and no matter what would come to happen here on Earth, I would be protected and cared for on another level. I never needed to worry. I think most of my brothers and sisters remembered Him too. Maybe all animals do.

I was growing fast. It did not take long to learn that I would not be a puppy forever. For a while my casual and carefree behavior was forgiven, but the day came all too soon when I found that I had to be accountable for my behavior. We entered into basic training in "How To Be A Good Dog". This was how I learned that I was a dog. I learned through class that I didn't just want to be a "dog", but I wanted to be a "good dog" too! We need to learn this early, for if we don't, we can spend the rest of our lives not knowing what we are.

I missed having time with my mother but the breeder man took care of everything. He rewarded us for playing nicely with each other, with other pets and with his kids. My bratty sister was a handful but he said that he had the right home all picked out for her, a home that needed an "alpha dog".

One of his kids really liked me. Even though I looked like all the rest, she liked me best. She would pet me and tell me "I Love You".

"Daddy," she said one day looking up at him hopefully, "Can we keep this one?"

I watched her face eagerly as she awaited his answer. I was learning to recognize when someone is happy or when someone is sad. She was not happy with his response. She cried because she wanted to keep me but her father the breeder man said "No". He said I would have to go to a new home. She looked at me through her little girl tears. It all reminded me of something precious in my deepest memory. The tears, the goodbye. Home.

One day one of the breeder man's little boys grabbed me roughly by the scruff of my neck and hurled me onto the ground. I think he thought I was a plaything. Much like my immature brothers and sisters, the boy was just too young to know any better. The breeder man, however, did not tolerate his behavior and saw this as an opportunity to teach the boy some manners. He took him by the scruff of the collar, but not in a mean way.

"How does this feel to you?"

The kid didn't answer. He was crying and ashamed that he'd been caught and that he needed to be taught this lesson. He knew he was wrong.

"...Doesn't feel very good does it?" The breeder man continued, "These pups have feelings too. Every single thing you do to them teaches them about love or about fear. What you did teaches fear!" He went on to say, "One moment of fear can impact a pup for the rest of its life. You must be careful! You must always teach love in everything you do, with dogs and with people too. In every moment of your life you make that choice. I want you to make the right choices. Always. Do you understand me?"

"Uh-huh," the boy mumbled, his head bowed to the ground. He would be okay. He had a good father to teach him right from wrong.

If we are not taught about love when our brains and hearts are forming, we may never even recognize it when it stands in front of us. We may even run from it. We would miss out on the one thing that makes life worth living. When we are raised with genuine love threaded through everything we do, love will always be threaded through everything we do.

Each of Us Unique

We were being groomed for our new homes. He couldn't keep all of us but I was hoping that he would keep me. I was glad that I was quiet and easy. There's no reason to be anything else. Some of my siblings had more immature souls. The man reprimanded them sharply if they barked too much or made too much noise or if they got too nippy with their new teeth. We all need to start somewhere. I was once where they were. As I observed them, I was glad to be me.

I started to realize how different we were from each other. The man had two legs and I had four. Those of us with four legs were different from each other too. I was starting to see that I was unique. I was learning that man was in charge.

We all received our vaccinations. The breeder man trained us as far as he could train us. The most important lesson of all had been to be cooperative and comfortable with humans because they are the reason we are here. Our Master creates us to give what most humans cannot give to each other. He created us to give unconditional love without judgment, love without limit. It is a bond. It is an important commitment we need to be prepared for. The breeder man prepared us well. It was getting to be time to move on.

Deja Vu

People started coming out to the barnyard to see us. I learned that I was a "Chocolate Lab." The man explained to the people that we would grow fast, be very smart; we might not live as long as other smaller breeds. I seemed to recall somehow that there was an important reason for me to be back at Rainbow Bridge. In the next thought I knew that I was too young to worry about any of this stuff.

Not too many days passed when a man came through the gate. It felt like I'd been there before. He looked at me with deep-set blue eyes. He focused on me and it was as if he knew me from somewhere even though we had never met.

He sat down on the grass with me and my brothers and sisters and quietly observed all of us. He kept looking at me. He kept running his hands through his salt and pepper hair. I don't know how I knew he would run his hands through his hair like that, but I knew that he would. I kept looking at him. It was like we remembered each other from another time and place.

"She's the one," he said. He picked me up and the way he held me, the way he looked at me, the way he spoke to me, I knew that I would be safe with him. I looked over at the breeder man's little girl who was crying again because she still wanted to keep me. It made me sad to see her cry because of me. I hoped that no one would ever cry again because of me. Somewhere long ago I remember bitter tears. I recalled a far away place where someone taught me to love and to recognize love.

"What's your name little girl?"

The man knelt down and looked at me with questions in his deep blue eyes. I didn't know the answer to his question. My goodness I didn't know my own name!

Suddenly in a flash of light and thought, I remembered her. Every cell in my being remembered every moment that I had shared with her. My mind had been cleared when I left her but somehow she was still inside of my heart a lifetime later. It is the heart that remembers things like this, not the memory centers of the brain. I could feel the love so strongly. I remembered it so clearly! I recognized it.

"I love you Jack. I love you..."

Still kneeling, the man reached out to me. I looked at him as I remembered her. I liked this nice man. It felt that I could learn to love him. He smelled like she did. He had the same heart. The same eyes. He must have had the same soul as she. Perhaps we are all in the same soul family. She was kneeling down the day she met me too, just like he was kneeling down here with me.

In the recesses of my mind I heard her calling my name. Sometimes "Jack" or "Jackie Blue" or "Jacka-Roo!" I loved all the names she gave to me.

Jack. I said to him. *My name is Jack.* He looked at me thoughtfully.

"You seem like a Jackie to me. I'm going to call you Jackie."

He pulled out a lightweight leash as the breeder man handed him some papers. I looked around. The little girl was still crying. Suddenly I had fear. Fear of change. The man was taking me away from everything I'd ever known. I looked back at my mother and my brothers and sisters. The breeder man. His kids. The boy who was mean to me. The barn. I was nervous. I didn't want to go. I ran over to the little girl and she hugged me and I licked her face. It made me feel better. I hope it made her feel better too.

The memories came to me again. Traces of this feeling. The experience of being somewhere that was home with someone I loved; somewhere that I could not stay.

Then, a wave of comfort washed over me as the man lifted me up and told me he was taking me home and that "Everything will be okay". It's like he read my mind. I read his mind and it was all desire, joy and love. I felt his good heart. He knew the need for comfort and care, and he could give it too.

From this moment on, I was his.

Going Home With Him

As soon as he opened the door to the rambling ranch house, I ran inside and checked out every corner of every room. When I got to the living room, I skidded to a stop. I was surprised to see a lady and a German shepherd sitting there together in a big lounge chair. Tentatively I went over to them. I couldn't smell them. I couldn't figure them out. She smiled and said, "It's okay little one" and the handsome shepherd wagged her tail. I felt very welcomed by them. It was as if I had seen both of them somewhere before.

"Jackie, come here!"

The man was friendly and excited as he entered the room. I looked at him. I didn't know what he wanted but he had a little piece of meat in his fingers. He offered it to me and I took it eagerly.

"You're going to have to learn some basic rules around here. You're not always going to get a free handout!" he laughed.

I looked over at the woman and the dog and they were ignoring us. The man didn't even seem to notice them there. I looked at him and back at them and then "poof!" they were gone from my sight. It was one of those things I didn't understand. Yet.

Chews and the Terrible Twos

We were settling into our new life. The man's name was Luke. Except for the lady and the dog, he was very much alone. He seemed quite alone even when they were around. He took very good care of me. I grew and learned to take care of him too.

We'd been together several months. My hair was growing in nice and thick. Not so long but soft and so shiny! Luke seemed to take such pride in me. He called me his "little girl." I found that I liked being a girl.

Over time I learned to be less clumsy. I developed some poise and a humble pride in myself. There was a bit of a tough time when my new teeth started coming in, but when he caught me chewing on his good leather glove, he started bringing home yummy doggie things to chew on instead. He always would adapt and learn and encourage me to do the right thing. A good master provides. I'm glad he gave me "chews" so that I no longer had to look for gloves and shoes.

"Don't worry, Jackie. This will pass and you will be so glad that you have strong healthy teeth!"

The days following were the most difficult for him and for me. He called it the "terrible twos" and it was way worse than gloves and shoes and chews! I was figuring out my place in the world; trying to learn where I ended and where he began. I was trying to figure out how much control I had in my life with him. Continually I tested him. Again and again I pushed the rules and the boundaries. It was only natural. I had given up my heavenly home with no limitations where the only rule was Love --- to come here to be with him. There were so many rules here! I wanted the only rule to be love. I wanted it all.

"The only control you really have, Sweetheart, is self-control. We're going to keep working on that."

He was a good teacher. I knew that I needed to learn how to live properly in this world so that I could live in this world with him. Him. My master. My alpha. It didn't matter what we did or where we went. He was my master and he came to mean everything to me. If he was not paying attention to me I could get into all kinds of trouble. I won't go into detail but let's just say that if we are not given something constructive to do, it is our nature to find something to do wherever we can find it. Usually we find it in the wrong places.

Healthy growing pups have a lot of energy and curiosity. We need to learn discipline. We need walks, runs, playtime, jobs, tasks, training classes and opportunities to meet others of our own kind and to get to know different kinds of people too.

Separation Anxiety II

Uh Oh. He was leaving me for the first time. He always worked from home but the day came when he had to leave and he couldn't take me with him. I was upset. I didn't know he would ever have to leave me.

"Sorry Sweetheart," he said, "but I'll be back soon." He knelt down and embraced me. 'I'll be back soon.' The words touched me deep in my soul and connected with faraway memories there.

"You take good care of the house while I'm gone." Closing the door behind him, he was gone and I was alone.

I had never been alone before. I ran into the other room to see if the lady and her dog were there as they so often were, but they were gone too. I ran window to window. I couldn't see him. If only I could see where he went! I had no way out. I don't know where I would have gone had I been able to get out. I didn't know how I would ever find him. There was food in my dish but I was not hungry. There was fresh water in my bowl but I wasn't thirsty. I went over to the chair where he always sat. I climbed into it and curled up there. His scent lingered there and that alone was reassuring.

I fell asleep and found myself in a world where I am never alone. She was there, the woman who loves me who lives in my heart, the one who never leaves.

We walked together through the Rainbow Forest. She talked with me and listened to me. I told her that I am lonely for her and she understood, for she was lonely too. She was beautiful and so full of light and love. I told her how beautiful she was. She knelt down in front of me and petted my head; her hands filled with the energy of the love in her heart for me. She said, "If I glow, it's because I love you so."

Oh I was so happy to be back where I belonged. I had no other thought but her and this place where I had total peace and comfort and love.

"I know I need to let you go," she said to me.

I didn't expect her to say that.

Oh no, I said. *Don't let me go. I've just now found you.*

"I'm trying, Jack, I really am," she said to me, fighting back the tears. I didn't know why she was crying. "I don't want to hold you back from anything. I know we are connected because I asked to dream of you today and here you are. You were always such a good boy."

Good Boy? I'm a 'good boy'? My mind started pondering. I thought I was a girl? I looked up then and she was gone. Not only that, but I found myself right back in my master's chair.

Had I not been thinking about whether I was a girl or not, I could have enjoyed more time with her. The confusion of the mind can create such disturbance in matters of the heart. While my dream with her was more real than the life I was living, the life I was living pulled me back when I focused on what mattered here. It took me away from her again.

My thoughts were interrupted by the sound of the key in the door. He was home! Yay! He was home! I then became cautious. It was not him at all. It was his sister, the one he called "Kelley."

"Hello precious!" she exclaimed when she saw me. She stood in the doorway looking at me, smiling. I wagged my tail even though I didn't understand. I wondered where he was and why she was here instead of him.

"I'll be staying here until Luke gets home. Don't worry, he'll be home soon."

Kelley liked me and it did not take me long to like and trust her too.

The next day she and I went outside and when we got there I saw the lady at the edge of the property throwing the ball to the German shepherd. Excitedly I ran out to see them. Kelley sharply called me back. I obeyed her. I figured I was not supposed to play with them.

Kelley looked at me tenderly. I could feel her heart song coming out of her eyes. She sat down on the porch steps and I sat quietly beside her there watching the lady and the German shepherd.

"Be patient with him little girl. He is just learning to love again. You think you need him, but he needs you more."

It's okay. I already made up my mind to love him no matter what. And I do. I love him.

Stress Looks in the Mirror

I worried about him. He wasn't happy but I didn't know why. I was doing a lot of barking since he left; I couldn't help myself. I would bark until I was exhausted and then I would have to go to sleep. I wanted to sleep because it made the time pass faster.

Kelley would look at me with concern. She often talked to me about him. She was full of worry because he was alone. He hadn't always been alone, so he was not very good at being alone. I understood because I had never been alone either and because it was new for me, I had been kind of nervous and scared until Kelley came to me to explain the situation.

"That's why he brought you home."

That was when I discovered that I had picked Luke too. I knew I had been sent here to watch over him and protect him but I could not fulfill this mission when he was gone from me. That is why I cried for him. That is why I cried for me.

Luke finally came home. I recognized his footstep the moment he stepped out of the car. When he came through the door I jumped all over him. I lunged for him and tried to kiss him wherever I found bare skin. Oh I was so happy he was home!!

"I am home little girl, I am here!" he said to me, for he was happy too.

That night I heard them talking about me, Kelley and Luke were trying to figure out how to 'deal with my behavior'.

"You can't be leaving her alone like that," she was saying to him. They labeled me with "separation anxiety," when I was just Luke's mirror. He brought me into his life to take care of me, but I came here to take care of him too. I had no way to protect him when he was away from me. They thought I needed help when he was the one who needed help because he was the one who had been left alone. He was the one who needed care.

Learning the Commands

My favorite friend at the park was the giant mulberry tree. It was always where I wanted to go first and Luke would always let me go. From the way it smelled, I knew it was where most of the dogs liked to start. I don't know why, but I just loved that tree! It's kind of like what happens when you meet a soul mate. You love them and you don't know why. You don't remember that they were once very important to you. He was the biggest tree in the park. He was the king of all the trees! I knew he was my soul mate.

After we stopped at the mulberry tree, we went across the park to Obedience Class. We would go there every Sunday. Oh I loved this place and the learning came easily to me. It was interesting. Just like it is with human students, some excel at class and some don't. Some of us have certain natural gifts that we bring with us from previous lives, much like the human Mozart, who composed symphonies at three years of age. We may not be as impressive as Mozart, but when something comes easily, it's how we know we have had previous training and expertise somewhere along the line. It runs through our blood and our DNA. Our previous lives are like dreams within a dream. We learn from each one and keep building on what we have learned until we know everything!

We were going through the basic commands. SIT. This park seemed so very familiar to me. STAY. I remembered her teaching me the same things. COME. He was pleased with my progress. WAIT. I had learned quickly. He rewarded me with treats and when the lessons were over he would always reward me with playtime.

I was a little tentative the first time but I got really good at swimming in the pond. I was surprised how I took to the water like a fish! Then I would play fetch with him. I'd go crazy chasing that ball! I could do it all day long! Then he would get kind of serious again so I was never sure if it was a lesson or a game, but we would play at tracking the Vienna Sausages downwind.

"Go Jackie Go!"

I was en route to the sausages! My nose pressed to the ground and downdraft from the meat, I picked up on the scent of lavender and pine. It was she. She filled my nose and then she filled every corner of my mind. I knew that she was near. I raised my nose to the wind as I scanned the park.

"Jackie, stay on task," he commanded sharply.

Given the choice I would have chosen her over the hotdogs any day, but I found the meat a few steps away and I ate it as my own reward. Luke then rounded me up and it was time to go home. I knew we'd come back to the park again soon.

224

A Test of Obedience

He had taken the day off. It was some kind of holiday and I was so glad to be able to go to the park again! I was learning about the change of seasons and I came to realize that I enjoyed leaving the hot season behind and moving into the coolness of fall. It was the kind of day she loved. I'd been thinking of her a lot since our last trip to the park. I had a dream again with her. I remembered it because I woke myself up out of it; my legs were running so fast to run to greet her.

The moment he opened the door of the truck, I jumped out with eagerness and curiosity. I smelled the breeze. I looked all around. I was on a mission. I was looking for her.

"Jackie, stay there!"

Sometimes I wished he would just talk to me like normal instead of ordering me around all the time like I'm just a dog. But it was okay. It was what it was and his heart was good. He had more to learn too. He snapped the leash on me and we headed on over to visit the mulberry tree. As we approached, in my mind's eye I saw her leaning, her back against the tree. I saw her there with me. My memories were strong.

Then. I couldn't believe my eyes. You can just tell by the way someone walks and holds their head and shoulders. When you know them intimately, you recognize their footsteps. Just beyond my tree, I saw her. She was walking away. I asked myself if I was dreaming, but I wasn't. As we passed by my tree, I could smell that she'd been sitting there on the big root that came out of the trunk. I couldn't help myself. I started to run to her so fast the leash slipped from Luke's hand. He was taken by complete surprise for I had never ever left his side.

He called my name. I felt fear in his voice.

"Jackie!"

I had always been obedient to him.

I had always been obedient to her. She was the stronger force in the moment. I keep running.

"Jackie come!"

She stopped and turned towards us at the sound of my name. She saw me. Our eyes locked. She already had tears, for tears always would come at the sound of my name and any other time she would be reminded of me.

I could not believe what was happening, that she was actually here with me! My head was filled with a rush of memories. I remembered everything about her, about us. I remembered it all so clearly. How could it be that this was she? It seemed a miracle!

He whistled for me. "Jackie! COME!"

I paused for a fleeting moment to look back at him. I turned and looked back at her. The breeze was behind her. I could smell her. Lavender. Pine.

"JACKIE!" He was getting really upset with me. I paid no heed. I had a flashback. She used to call me Jackie too. She always said that a dog needed to have a two-syllable name in order to be able to get its attention. I was flooded with the memories of the life we had lived together.

I skidded to a stop. She stood before me with a look on her face that was hard to describe. I couldn't tell if she was sad or if she was happy.

"Hi Baby."

She was talking to me; jolting me back to reality. Reality such as it was. She always called the dogs she didn't know 'Baby'. I don't know why. I guess it's probably because she didn't know their names but she loved them nonetheless. It seemed very endearing. I always wanted her to call me that, but she never did. Not until this moment. She looked at me with those kind and compassionate eyes and she was calling me 'Baby' too.

There was something missing. She was different than I remembered. Did the loss of me change her so much? She was calmer. Quieter. More reserved and proper. Kind of like when you are meeting someone for the first time. I wondered what was wrong. Maybe she was depressed because I had left her.

Suddenly I came to realize that she didn't recognize me. In that moment I was just another "Baby"; another dog whose name she didn't know. She didn't know my name and she didn't know who I was. How could she? I hadn't yet thought about how different my body must have looked from the body I wore when I was hers. I remembered my long shaggy blonde hair. I remembered I was really big! I did not know how to let her know that I was me.

He was coming closer. I was thinking really fast, trying to think of something, anything, to let her know who I was. Then I did what I so often did before. I pushed my nose into her hand and love-nibbled the sleeve of her jacket, pulling her gently along with me towards Luke. Tugging at her sleeve, I led her to him.

She looked a little like a deer in headlights, but she went along with me nonetheless. She squinted as if she was trying to remember something that happened long ago. Or maybe she just had the sun in her eyes.

"What are you DOING?!" Luke threw his hands up in the air in frustration. "You COME when you're called! You leave this nice lady alone." He was very upset with me for disobeying him. He was firm with me but he was still really kind.

He looked apologetically at her. "I'm sorry," he said to her. "She doesn't usually act like this. She always comes when she is called. I've never seen her do this before."

"It's okay. No harm done," she replied to him as her eyes searched his face. She remembered him.

"I know you," he says.

"Yes."

Meanwhile I was looking at her. I wanted her to look at me but she was looking at him. It was a nice moment. Even though they ultimately went their separate ways again after exchanging a few niceties, I realized that something of the Grand Scheme had taken place and it didn't have anything to do with me. Or did it?

Soul mates meet in a place where time stands still. You recall where you were when the call came in. The vivid colors of the day. The season. The way the sun was streaming in or how the rain fell upon the glass. That's how you know it was your destiny. You can remember the smallest details of your meeting. And you thought it wouldn't matter.

In a split second, we fall in love, we break up, and we live out a love story that lasts until the end of time. We are soul mates, we are adversaries; we are everything. We are nothing. We are at our fullest potential of every possibility. We are supposed to cross paths for one reason or another. Sometimes we don't know the reason until it's all behind us.

In Memoriam

Time had passed. It was another beautiful day. We were together and heading to the park. I couldn't wait; my head was out the window already sniffing for the sausages and the mulberry tree. Maybe even she would be there.

As we pulled into the parking lot, the uniformed landscape committee was preparing the area. Big trucks were backing in.

"Excuse us, clear the way!" hollered the uniformed workers. They had helmets on. Then they started up the chain saw. They approached my friend the mulberry tree and they began to cut it down branch by beautiful branch.

THUMP! WHUMPH!

We were both in shock. We watched them as they took the giant tree down. Each branch landed heavily onto the ground below. Branch fell upon branch fell upon branch. I don't know why I was so sad about this. Each branch that fell made me sadder and sadder. It felt like I was saying goodbye to an old friend. It took quite awhile; the tree was so big.

WHUMPH! Another huge branch fell from the tree.

I remembered something far in the recesses of my mind. She was there, the woman I love. She was pruning the roses in the garden and crying as each rose bled, sticky white. She held each one as she made the fatal cut and then comforted each of them saying, "I'm sorry. I'm so sorry."

THUMP!

Roses feel no pain. The tree, made of 100% spirit felt no pain either, although it would have been more respectful of those who were cutting it to have done this in the winter while the tree was sleeping. I found myself wondering if anyone had ever thought to ask the tree if it was okay or to let the tree know what was going to happen to it. No matter who we are, it's always easier for us to let go of this life when we have some advance preparation, whether mammal or mulberry tree.

We all are spirit and consciousness, but each man and animal has a brain. Pain is located in the brain. Plants, while they have intelligence and wisdom, do not have a physical brain. A brain is where the pain receptors are located. So while she cried over those roses, projecting her own thoughts of what it would be like to have her own arm cut off each time she cut a stem, the plant was feeling more like it was having a hair cut. All those wasted tears!

Plants can feel pressure and emotion. When something is said or done with intention, a plant can respond. So every day we tell our tree that it is beautiful, it will get more and more beautiful. I hope that tree knew how beautiful I thought it was.

When the cutting crew stopped to take a break, Luke approached them.

"Why are you taking out this beautiful tree?" he inquired.

They reported that they had built the pond too close to the tree and the tree's roots were growing through the concrete shell of the pond and causing leaks. So they plant a tree and build a pond and then cut the tree down?

"That's tragic," said Luke, shaking his head.

"It's just a tree," the guy holding the chain saw said, shrugging.

Just a tree? Am I just a dog?

"It's just the way it is," the park guy said. "This tree has shed so many leaves, it's just a damn nuisance."

I didn't understand how they could plant a tree and then complain about it.

The men went back to work. I watched the tree. I watched the workers. I wondered why human be-ings have such a hard time letting things "be".

I always enjoyed studying languages and I learned from my Master that He wanted humans to be called Human Beings to continually remind them that they are really verbs and that their soul purpose is to BE. I think they tend to forget about this, they are so busy being nouns doing things that won't matter tomorrow.

I watched Luke watching the tree. I watched the tree and the men who disassembled it. When the sawdust had settled, Luke went over to talk to the park guy. He wanted to plant a tree in place of the one they had taken down. This made me very happy. This made my friend the mulberry tree happy too.

When the last of the debris was hauled away, they carefully planned the best place to put another tree. In the very center of the park, they outlined a place where the new tree would be planted. The following weekend Luke and I went to the nursery and picked out the healthiest, largest mulberry tree we could find.

"It will grow very fast and strong," the nursery guy told us. "It's the best shade tree there is and it's a great value for the price."

We put the tree in the back of our truck along with some bags of compost and other stuff that makes a tree grow big and strong. Off we went with our new tree, back to the park. Some guys were raking up remnants of the mulberry tree and Luke asked them if we could use some of the bark and remains to plant with the new tree.

"Sure, no problem."

They helped him to dig a big hole and a little while later the new tree was in. Piled around the surface was the compost from the old tree to feed the new tree. Luke then went back to the truck, pulled out a hammer and a flat shiny rectangular thing and went over to the base of the tree. He pounded a gold nameplate on a bracket into the ground. It read: "IN MEMORY OF AUDREY CARPENTER".

He then sat down near the newly planted tree and I sat down beside him. I looked over at the tree and decided that I would call it Grandfather Tree, in honor of the King of Trees. I would tell it every day how big and beautiful it is!

"What do you think, Jackie? Do trees go to Heaven too?" Luke asked me.

With watery eyes, Luke was not really looking for an answer from me. His mind was already somewhere else in another place and time. The mind always follows the eyes and his eyes had a sorrowful and faraway look. I knew he was missing someone. I had learned this from watching her miss me.

Hitting Bottom

Luke would read out loud every so often to me. Sometimes he would talk to me about Heaven and 'her'. He still thought that Heaven was a place unto itself. A place where angels play harps and flutes while lounging around on fluffy clouds where God presides over all with flowing beard and robe.

People often look up into the sky and look for their loved ones there. They see clouds that pass and sometimes they find their loved ones in the clouds. Those clouds are God's gifts to help them to keep the faith that life is far from over when life ends upon the earth. He tells them this: Whatever they seek, they will find. If they are seeking their loved ones in the sky, He will send them clouds so they will find them there. If they seek discord, they will find it. If they seek love, the most precious thing of all, they will be blessed with it. Love and wisdom are the only things you take with you from lifetime to lifetime.

The winter evenings were long and lonely for him. One night he was sitting in his leather easy chair. The winds were blowing cold outside. There was a fire in the fireplace and I was lying at his feet. It should have been a peaceful night.

I heard him blow his nose and I looked up at him and saw that he was crying. When he saw me looking at him he reached down and ruffled the hair on the top of my head. Then he pulled his hand away and he started to weep. It made me so sad when he was so sad. He was sad a lot. There seemed to be nothing I could do to comfort him.

"Whatever will I do, Jackie? If I didn't have you I wouldn't want to go on." He slid out of his chair and down onto the floor beside me. He surprised me by putting his arms around me as he cried into my fur. I licked the tears from his face.

"She was only 45. You would have loved her. She made this house complete. She made everything wonderful."

He told me how they married young. Many years later they tried to have a baby but there were complications and they lost it. He kept weeping. He had so many tears! I wanted to tell him that I knew of a mother in the whelping box who lost her children too. I wanted to tell him that everything works out. I wanted to let him know that somewhere there was a good reason for it. I didn't know how to tell him. He was crying too hard for his heart to hear anything but his own pain.

"My wife is dead. My baby's dead..." His body wracked with sobs as he rocked back and forth. He was not the one rocking. The angels, the wife, the baby were rocking him, trying to comfort him. He needed all of them. He was hitting bottom.

Oh my friend, they are not dead.

———

"My dog is dead too," he whined.

They are not dead. They are not dead!

I rested my chin on his knee.

They are not dead. They are alive.

How to tell him I had seen them here? Right there in our living room!

He stood up and blew his nose on his handkerchief before walking over to take a framed picture from off the mantle. He looked at it thoughtfully and wiped his nose again as he returned to the floor with me at the foot of his chair.

He showed her to me and there she was. I recognized her instantly! She was the lady who was sitting in the living room the first day I entered the house. In the picture next to her was the German shepherd; the one who was with the lady that night and the other times I had witnessed them.

"I lost our Thalia too, just a few months later."

Thalia is not lost. You are the one who is lost.

"I've lost everything that I've loved."

You haven't lost anything.

As he held the picture close to his chest, he wept. I just sat there and looked at him, wanting to help but not knowing how. He could not seem to hear me.

"I've lost everything," he kept saying over and over. "Everything. Everything I ever loved."

Then he paused and looked over at me, tears quietly streaming down his face. He realized he had forgotten all about me.

"Oh Jackie. I'm sorry you came along right in the middle of all this. You're such a good girl. I know I say I've lost everything but I have you now. I have you," and he hugged me so tight that I could hardly breathe.

"She told me she wanted me to love again. I never loved anyone but her, you know. I don't know how to love again. Maybe you can help me."

Later I kept watch over him from the floor beside his bed as he slept. The framed picture was still in his hands; he held it close to his chest. Finally he entered the land of dreams and then I went to sleep.

I found myself dreaming too. I was running with my friend Thalia. She and I were at Obedience Training at the park near Grandfather Tree. Then something happened and she and I were passing in the hallway at the veterinarian's office, our eyes lingering on one another. Next thing I knew, we were frolicking to and fro across the Rainbow Bridge. I looked back at her one final long loving look, before I ran back across the Bridge, leaving her on the other side. I asked to be able to remember this dream so that I could always remember my promise when I wake up. I also asked to remember so that I could be sure to remember Thalia too, for she is the one who sent me to him.

There was a very good reason why I was there with Luke and Luke was there with me.

Dreams are Teachers Too

Kate always kept a dream journal by her bed and she always wrote down her dreams. Sometimes they did not make any sense until a long time later when she would look back on them and she could then see the messages based on how her life had unfolded.

One dream was especially interesting. She had it quite some time after I had made my journey to Rainbow Bridge, but I was right there in the dream along with other spectators and I saw it all unfold before my eyes.

Time had passed and she was kind of taking Joey for granted. This particular night she went to sleep and as morning approached she had a vivid dream. Those of us who know how to navigate Dreamland know how important it is to visit early in the darkness of morning, because the dreamer more easily remembers a dream if it takes place near the time of waking. Sometimes we will even make something happen to wake the dreamers up so that they are sure to remember that we were there. Dreams are the meeting places of the soul and souls on all levels in all places can connect in Dreamland, where anything can happen.

In her dream, Joey had been hit by a big old   black truck while crossing a three-lane highway. There were a bunch of young guys all dressed in black inside the truck and they were laughing their heads off as they ran over him. She watched it all happen. She raced out into the middle of the highway to gather him up. She cared nothing for her own safety. Joey's legs were all mangled and his eyes, which had always been fixed so lovingly upon her, were unresponsive. She could only watch as he died in her arms. "Oh nooooo! Oh Joey! I love you I love you! Joey! Joey!" she was crying.

When she woke up a split second later, she found Joey lying there comfortably on the bed next to her. He was looking up at her with his big dark eyes, so filled with love for her. As always, he had those beautiful eyes shining with the love of his tender and enthusiastic soul.

"Oh Joey, I'm so glad you're okay!" she said as she picked him up and smothered him with kisses.

Joey wasn't surprised at all. He had created that dream. He did it for her and he did it for himself. He was in the dream with her and he created the drama of his own death because he needed the reassurance from her that he was loved. When the dream was over, he saw that he was. Mission accomplished.

It's a lot like the dream of life. When you finally wake up, you find the love you thought you were missing.

Leaving the Comfort Zone

She was getting dressed up real pretty for the annual Hospice fundraising dinner. She knew a lot of people there. It was a fancy sit-down dinner with cocktails and nice music playing. When it was time for dinner to be served, she located the place at a table reserved with her name. As she was sitting down, she looked around. To her left was her coworker, Rosemarie. To her right sat her coworker, Ron, and his wife. She almost fell off her chair when she looked before her and found herself sitting directly across the table from him. Luke. Salt and Pepper.

"What on earth is he doing here?" she asked herself.

The questions in her head and the feelings in her heart were louder than the keynote speaker and more powerful than the music. While she tried to focus on the discussion panel on the stage nearby, her mind was processing LUKE. She didn't realize it, but he was doing the very same thing with her. A couple of times they caught glimpses of each other's glimpses. They both seemed to be going through the motions of the evening, hardly tasting their beautifully catered dinner. They each had a second glass of wine. After dinner there was an auction to raise funds and then the band began to play again.

He approached her. She saw him coming towards her and her heart was in her throat. He was so nervous that it felt like everything was in slow motion, like a scene from a movie. That's what Living in the Moment can feel like. He arrived at her side and he held out his hand and asked her to dance. She put her hand in his and they went out onto the dance floor. The last time she had danced, she danced with Mr. Monkey, so she was pretty nervous about that.

"How is it that we are both in this same place together tonight?" she enquired.

"It must be divine intervention," Luke replied.

They danced well together. It was a sign. She felt at home in his arms and he in hers. She was still bothered by the gold band on his left hand. She didn't want to spoil the evening. She didn't want to ask him. She didn't want the answer. She didn't want to make him uncomfortable by looking to him for an answer. She wanted to keep the fairy tale going. She feared that the question would be the beginning of the end.

They danced, fast songs, slow songs and in between songs. She tried to push the questions from her mind and just enjoy the moment, but it was hard. Her fear was getting in the way. She knew she would have to say something. When the last song of the set ended, they had a little talk.

"This is the best time I've had in a long time," he said to her. "I don't get out much."

"I'm having a wonderful time too..."

He could feel that she had something more to say and it made him nervous. He had already started falling for her. He braced himself for the crash.

"But...?" He was making it easy for her.

"Oh Luke. Why are we having such a lovely time dancing," she paused to get her breath, "...when you are married."

He let out a long sigh. She braced herself for his answer. An answer she was not expecting.

Over the course of that evening they learned a lot about each other. He learned that she had devoted her life to her work with hospice. She learned that he had had a wife whom he loved very much. Audrey had been a hospice patient. He had cared for her at home until she passed, more than two years before. It turned out that he and Kate had zigged and zagged even over the course of their time at Hospice. They were always just a degree of separation away from each other and yet they never once crossed paths.

The two were so absorbed in their conversation that it caught them off-guard to see that the place had cleared. They were the last guests there, so it was time to leave. Without a word, they walked together to her car, which just so happened to be parked beside his.

Her mouth was quiet but her heart was full and her mind was active. After all the comings and goings between them, she did not want to let him just walk away again. She was feeling desperate because her own abandonment issues were rearing their heads. She would always ask herself what Jack would do in certain situations. She had learned from me how to be honest, open and genuine. As she was preparing, the situation took care of itself.

"I'm not going to lose you again," Luke said to her as he placed his business card into her hand, cupping her fingers around it. "My home number is on there too."

He then kissed her in the space between her cheek and her lips and left her standing there, leaning on the edge of the open car door, still deprogramming her overactive brain.

As he lay awake much of that night, she lay awake much of the night too. Something had changed inside of her. She looked over at Immy and Joey as they lay sleeping beside her in her big bed. She thought back to Robert and Shane and Benjamin. She knew it had not been love.

She dreamed of Luke.

Interruption

Her hands were trembling as she dialed his home number. It rang once. Twice. She cleared her throat. Three times. On the fourth ring the voice mail answered. It was a woman's voice.

"Luke and Audrey aren't home right now, but leave us a message and we'll be sure to call you back!" the voice said, cheerfully.

She hung up the phone so fast, as if she had touched a hot stove. It caught her off guard. It felt so awkward.

"What do I do with this?" she asked herself.

She thought of the wedding band. What if he was lying? But what would he gain by lying? She went through all the deliberations. If he wasn't lying, she knew enough about grief to know that he couldn't possibly be ready to meet someone new if he was still clinging to his wife. It could never work. He had not removed her voice from their outgoing message or his band from his hand. Keep in mind that you cannot see something in someone else if you don't have it yourself. He was not the only one who wasn't ready for the relationship.

She studied his card. He was an attorney in private practice. What she didn't know was that Luke was one of the biggest benefactors of the Hospice Foundation. Yes, his wife Audrey had crossed over Rainbow Bridge quite some time ago. Yes, he was still very much in love with her. He wore his wedding band because he had not detached from her and he felt he needed something tangible to keep her close to him and to remind him of their eternal bond. Yes, her voice was still on their voicemail because he simply couldn't bring himself to erase her.

Many men have a strong tendency to want to be with a woman again after death or divorce and he was starting to think about what was next. It was just the beginning of the journey for him. After all, he was very much alone. He had not yet thought about how wedding bands and voicemails could deter someone. He wasn't thinking clearly yet.

He kept thinking of Kate. He would sometimes imagine bringing her into his life and filling it up with love and alive-ness again. Then he would immediately feel guilty for feeling those feelings.

"Who do you think you are?" he would say critically to himself. "Your wife has died and you are already looking at another woman!" He was not sure where this thought came from. He was thinking maybe it was the devil in his head wanting to be sure that he would never be happy again. He kept coming home hoping to find a message from her, but there was no message.

Love has a timeframe all of its own and love never dies. It is eternal. There is no end. There is no rush. There is no hurrying it. It waits patiently. It waits because it knows that there is no end and that like the sea it comes and goes.

Conversations with Dog

"Oh Jackie," Luke said, "What's happening to me? Audrey told me she wants me to love again but I feel I am betraying her to want to love again. What am I supposed to do?"

You're supposed to love. It's why you're here.

"I don't deserve to be happy."

You deserve to be happy.

"I'll never get over this."

Yes you will.

"She was the love of my life. If I never love again she was enough."

You can't see it now but you won't grieve forever. Life goes on, it always does. She taught you to love so that you would love again.

"How can so much time have passed when it seems like yesterday?"

Because time doesn't exist.

I knew he was healing. When he confused the concept of time and started thinking that no time had passed at all, this was the clue.

Kate was healing too, asking me the very same things. Audrey was the love of Luke's life and, thus far, I was the love of hers.

"Am I betraying you to want another?"

You're supposed to love a human being in this life.

"I'm not sure I deserve to be happy."

Oh yes, you do.

"I'm not sure I'll ever get over this."

Yes you will. Your new love will heal you the rest of the way. He needs you too.

"Jack you were the love of my life. If I never have love again, you were enough."

I came here to teach you love! What good is learning something if you never use it? I'm asking you to love again.

Obstacles

Scrolling through his old messages, he heard the caller on the other end hang up without leaving one. He looked at the call ID. He recognized the interchange. He knew it had been her. For days and days he contemplated calling her number and day after day the shameful voice in his head would talk him out of it.

One day he took in a deep breath and he rose above the shaming voice. He picked up the phone and dialed her number. He tried to swallow but he couldn't and he had a hard time getting his breath. That's how you know the potential of love is there, waiting to be expressed. It was so big it was like it was trapped in his throat.

"Hello" said the voice on the other end.

"Hi..." he began nervously, but he had received her voicemail.

"...Jack and Kate aren't home right now, but we'll call you back just as soon as we can."

She had never changed her message either because she hadn't quite let go of me. It had just seemed so final to change our message too. This is an example of how refusing to change can get in the way of things that are waiting for you. The kaleidoscope turns but it is all a part of the bigger picture that is fully and beautifully designed by our Creator.

He quietly hung up the phone, disappointed. It seemed that Kate already had a guy named Jack. Of course she would. He fondled the wedding band on his finger. He had been so absorbed in worrying about what she thought of him that he didn't think for a moment about what might be going on with her.

The timing just wasn't right. She thought she was ready but she wouldn't be ready to move forward until she released her attachment to me. He thought he was ready too but a big reason for the obstacles was because Audrey wasn't ready to let go of him. He had clung to her and she was still clinging to him too. He would not be free to be with someone new until she was willing to let go of him from beyond the grave. Her letting go of him was what he needed to be able to let go of her.

The seed had been planted. It was the beginning. He was thinking about love again.

Love Always Gives
Love Never Dies

I knew the woman he loved was watching all of this just as I would watch Kate from beyond Rainbow Bridge.

Audrey was still in the house with him. I knew this because I'd seen her there. She had not yet committed to going all the way into Heaven because this would mean that she would need to release him from her grasp. She was obviously visiting from the Healing Center. It was the only way something like this could happen. She was in limbo and she kept him in limbo in the process.

I would see glimpses of her as she walked through our kitchen. She always entered through the garage door, as they always had when she walked the earth. She always left through the front door, which was a little strange because they had rarely used the front door.

Sometimes he would invite me to get up onto the bed with him at night but I wouldn't because sometimes she would be lying there beside him. I never quite knew who she was, but I knew he loved her and if he loved her then I would love her too and honor the space they shared.

"What am I to do Jackie?" he asked me once, turning his gaze upon me as if I had all the answers. "How do I get through this?"

Just believe. No tears, for they will break the spell. She will do what you ask of her just like she always did.

One night quite some time after the Hospice event and the phone calls, she came to him in a transparent glow of light. She stood over him and then she gently placed her hand upon his shoulder as he was reading. She leaned down and kissed his cheek and then she was gone as soon as she came. Like a dream, an apparition, he did not see her, but I did. I knew that somewhere in his being he knew she had been present with him, for right after she left he glanced up from the paper and gazed out the window without really seeing anything there. He knew that something significant had happened.

Like a dream, the unspoken message can reach the depths of the soul and circumvent the mind. Audrey had come to tell him something very important. By doing so, she freed herself to enter the gates of Heaven. She had come to give him permission to let her go.

Revisiting Einstein

My favorite scientist of all time is Einstein. I got to know him in Heaven's realm. My love for him drew him to me right after I crossed the Bridge. He taught me a lot. He helped me to understand quantum studies, which is what led him to receive the Nobel Prize in Theoretical Physics when he worked on the earth.

In electromagnetics, photons and electrons can be in an infinite number of places at once. Highly developed telescopes have witnessed universes far beyond this one – thousands if not millions of them. We can go to all of them anytime we want.

What some scientists don't realize is that quantum physics applies to all of us. When we are stripped down to the root of our consciousness, somewhere in the unchartered territories of the 92% of the brain that we can't seem to access, we too can be in an infinite number of places at once.

The spirit can make anything happen when it's driven by love. Love is the power. This is how it can be that while I am here with Luke I have never really left Kate's side. Like Benito who was connected with Kate on a very deep level of knowingness, a part of me took up residence inside of her heart so that we would never be apart. This is how I can remember so many things – because I carry her heart and the memory of our love together, forever.

When Audrey makes entrance into Heaven, she and Thalia will reconnect with Luke at a higher and healthier level of vibration and love. They will be joined together by unconditional love that does not cling.

Leading Him to Her

She and Immy and Joey were at the park one Autumn Day. My friend Grandfather Tree was growing. It was about twelve feet tall and almost as wide. On this day there was a carpet of leaves all around. They had just come back from a hike along the river and she was sitting at the base of the tree brushing the weeds out of Immy's coat. So many people avoid the most beautiful places because they don't want weeds, but wherever you go there will always be some weeds of one kind or another.

Meanwhile Luke was at home working at his desk on his computer, very frustrated over some case he was trying to solve. I didn't like to see him frustrated, so I went over to him. With my leash in my mouth, I just quietly stood beside him. He glanced down at me.

"Oh," he said to me, "I suppose you want to go to the park now."

He refocused on his computer. I just stood there beside him for a little while longer. It would only be a matter of time.

"You sure know how to pick the best time to interrupt me," he said to me, smirking.

His hand reached out and petted my head, which now was at table height instead of at his knees. I persisted. He finally closed up the computer and delighted me by saying, "Let's go Jackie."

We drove to the park. I knew she would be there. I jumped out of the car and eagerly ran to the Mulberry Tree.

There she was. And Immy and Joey too. Just as I knew they would be. Still hanging out on the carpet of leaves at the base of our new favorite tree.

She stood up tentatively, as if she couldn't believe her eyes. Many months had passed. I was so much bigger but he was the same. His heart was the same. And so was hers.

As we approached the tree, he dropped the leash so I could run over and see Immy and Joey and so that when he got to her he could put his arms around her. Hers went around him too. It was like a movie, that's how I knew it was real. The two of them surrounded by our four-legged love under Audrey's mulberry tree, it's big heart-shaped leaves falling all around them and onto the ground.

"I've missed you."

"I've missed you too."

They vowed that day that they would stay together, finish working through their remaining grief and find a way to begin a new life.

There was love in the air and love in our hearts and love all around. And it was good.

Growing Together

We all started meeting at the park on a regular basis. She would always bring a thermos of coffee, ginger cookies for him and her and pumpkin cookies for Joey and Immy and me. I remembered those cookies; they were my favorites from my life before.

They had fun together. He needed it; she needed it. I needed it too. One day she breathlessly sat down on a big rock along the edge of the river after having laughed all the way down the path with him. I liked the fact that they made each other laugh. Then, a sudden shadow crossed over her face as she looked at the sun filtering through the trees. I had just arrived at her side and Luke was coming up from behind us with Immy and Joey who were walking with him.

She reached her arm out to me and put it around my neck the way she used to do before when I was her Jack. Oh I found I still loved her as much as ever. I nuzzled her playfully for I loved how she loved me. I loved how she held me.

I spoke to her, my heart to hers. I forgot who I was for just a moment. I was dog. I was soul. I was Jack. I was Jackie. I was his. I was hers.

The heart always speaks the truth. The head can be filled with fear and distraction. It can overwhelm and trample the soul and prevent one from knowing what they really want. The mind chatter can get in the way of being in the right place at the right time to make the right decisions.

They were both learning how the heart holds all the knowledge of the universe. Most people barely scratch the surface of what the heart contains. They don't get out of their overanxious minds. They don't even realize that the entire universe resides right inside the heart. They don't seem to understand that that is where everything is waiting for them.

The day came when he showed her the photos that he had shown to me. He was practicing sharing them when he shared them with me and now he was ready to open up to her. She was making coffee in the kitchen and he was laying out the photos and the albums on the table.

When she brought their coffees into the living room, she immediately saw the photo of Audrey and Thalia. She almost dropped the teacups. She set them down with an unintentional "clunk" as her mouth dropped open.

"Oh my gosh. Is that your wife? That's Thalia! Oh my goodness Luke, that's your wife?" She recognized Audrey right away because Audrey was the one who'd brought Thalia to training class. Audrey was the one who got tangled up with Kate in our leashes.

Luke had occasionally referred to her by name but, as things go, Kate never knew Audrey's name and Audrey never knew hers. They only knew Jack and Thalia.

"Yes, that's Audrey," he replied to her.

He quickly turned the next page of the album. Then, thinking better of it, he turned the page back and then closed up the book.

"We'll save the old days for some other time," he remarked.

She knew he was uncomfortable and she wanted to help shift the conversation. On the coffee table was a small crystal bowl with a dozen or so shiny dimes inside of it.

"So what's with the bowl full of coins?" she asked him.

"Oh that. I find a dime here and there, every so often and when I do I always bring it home and put it in this bowl. It reminds me of our college days when I would always make sure she had a dime in her purse so that she could call me from the dormitory pay phone. Remember when a phone call was only a dime?"

He seemed to think it was ironic that he kept finding really shiny dimes.

"Maybe she's reaching out to you. To make sure you think of her or, perhaps, to make sure you always have a dime so you can call on her whenever you need her."

I thought he might look at her like she was nuts but he looked at her with his blue eyes wide.

"My goodness I never ever thought of that," he said. "It makes perfect sense. I never started finding them until she was gone." He looked away pensively, trying to process this new revelation. He recalled how once he even found a dime in between the sheets on his bed.

"I never keep money in the bedroom."

"Well there's your evidence," Kate stated.

They sat there quietly beside each other. He thought of Audrey and the dimes; she thought of feathers and lizards and goose bumps.

"It's so crazy how time passes," Kate said to him, breaking the silence. "In the blink of an eye we are young and then all too soon we are old."

He didn't say anything. There would be time. There would be time to tell her everything, but for now he just told her how glad he was that she came into his life when she did.

"If you'd come any earlier, I might have had to leave Audrey for you!"

He laughed and she did too. It was the kind of laughter that brought a much-needed release. When he thought about what he had just said, he felt really bad...but he had laughed and it felt good after crying for so long.

Their relationship was becoming more and more serious. It was difficult to keep focused on the heart all the time as little aggravations would come up now and again, but they were doing really well together.

Because they were connected, heart and soul, when she healed, he healed too. When you are connected to someone, no matter what side of the Bridge you are on, whatever you are feeling will impact the other. Whatever you learn will impact the other. Whatever you love will impact the other.

"I need to warn you," Kate said to him "that I'm really independent, probably to a fault. I never needed anyone. I am not proud. I've lost my house I have nothing to offer but my love."

"It's perfect," he replied. "I've lost my love and have nothing to offer but my house."

He smiled a gentle smile. Hope had returned to his heart.

The Heart Speaks

Everything comes around again in another form. One year had passed since the Hospice fundraiser. They now had their own voices on their voicemail messages. They still led separate lives but every week or so they would get together for dinner or a walk in the park and talk about life. Their relationship was growing slowly over time. The strongest things often take the longest time to grow. Over time they had healed significantly with one another's help, even though he still wore his wedding band. Their love was unconditional for each other.

It was again time for the Hospice event. They sat together, this time on the same side of the table. As they chatted enthusiastically with the other guests, she could see that he was healing, for she was surprised that he was so much more outgoing than she. He was coming out of his shell of grief. The more she got to know him the more she fell in love with him.

When there was a lull in the conversation after dinner, the dance music beckoned the two of them out to the floor. She wasn't nervous this time; nor was he.

As they began to dance she turned her face to him to say something.

"Shhh," he said, putting his finger to her lips. "We need no words. Let's just live in the moment and enjoy the dance." She was taken aback, realizing that he'd finally learned the language of the heart.

Those who are arrogant and controlling are determined to cling to spoken words but peaceful hearts are unafraid to go deeper beneath the surface. This is why I chose him for her. I knew she was ready for a higher love and I knew in his heart that he was almost ready too.

They danced in a world of their own until the music stopped. In the brief hours with him she learned how powerful silence could be. It fascinated her as she swirled in the silent vortex of a waltz while the world chattered on beyond the dance floor. She felt the great power of the heart, for that is what speaks when the mouth is shut and the brain is at bay. They had both been given a gift for all that they had learned.

As I have said before, Nothing is ever all good or all bad. Kate looked around for something good that had come out of her losses. She didn't expect to see too much. Then! Then all of a sudden she saw Luke. She felt the potential of great love in her heart. She saw a book. She saw people who had come to love my book and me. She saw friends she would not otherwise have known. She saw you. She saw with new eyes and now she thinks with her heart instead of her head...just the way I taught her to do.

Life Begins Again

Not long after the hospice dinner he called her. They started going out on a more regular basis. His nervousness was gone and so was hers. By getting to know each other and growing slowly in love, they were healing their hearts.

This particular night he invited her to his house for dinner. He wanted the night to be perfect and he insisted on picking her up. He had his dining room set up like an Italian Restaurant. He knew her favorite meal was spaghetti and meatballs and salad and wine. He made extra meatballs for Joey and Immy and me. He even had the red and white-checkered tablecloth on the table and Italian romance music filled the room.

The night was a success but it wasn't over yet. He drove her home and I was glad when he invited me to come along. She invited him in as she always does now. Joey jumped all over us when we first came through the door and Immy squealed with delight to see Kate – and to see Luke there too. She didn't give me the time of day, just a sidelong glance so I would know she knew that I was there.

"Look at how Immy is so smitten with you now," Kate commented to Luke. "She was never crazy for anyone but me."

"I'm crazy for you too," he said, winking at her as he went over to light a fire in the fireplace. Of course all of us who are watching from the edge of Rainbow Bridge get excited when we see the metaphors taking place. It's how we speak. He lights her fire. We all look at each other, proud of ourselves because we know that our plan has been successful.

As he stoked the fire she prepared a pot of spiced tea. Pausing for a moment, she thought of how traditional the scenario was: woman in the kitchen, man stoking the fire. She smiled. It felt good. She found some ginger cookies that she had saved for special occasions. How did she know this would be a special occasion?

Us dogs were stretched out comfortably in the warm glow of the fire. Luke sat close to her on the couch as she poured the tea for both of them. As she offered him a cookie from the plate, he took the whole plate from her and placed it on the coffee table. Slowly and deliberately he turned to look straight at her. Blue eyes gazing into blue eyes.

"Is there something wrong?" she asked him, tentatively.

"Oh there's nothing wrong at all. I've just been meaning to tell you something for quite some time..."

He reached over with his right hand and twisted the wedding band off of his left hand in one smooth motion and slid it into his pocket. I was watching the whole thing intently. She knew as well as I did how significant this moment was for him. She didn't have words. There were no words. The power was strong between them.

He then reached into his coat pocket and pulled out a small piece of cloth. Unwrapping it revealed a beautiful diamond cocktail ring.

"Would you be willing to give me your hand?"

Metaphors. We loved this part!

She was struck by the intensity of the moment and the beauty of the diamond and was still recovering from seeing him remove his wedding band.

Give him your hand.

As she offered him her left hand, he placed the ring on her finger much like the prince had placed the perfectly fitting slipper on Cinderella. It was another sign. The ring fit perfectly because they were a perfect fit.

"We both know it's the right thing," he said to her with surety.

She put her arms around him.

"I'm so proud of you," she said.

"I'm proud of us," he replied as he gave her a kiss worthy of stage and screen. Even Immy and Joey gave a flip of their tails to show their approval.

Life is an illusion but it can be an exciting fairy tale if you follow your heart as you travel through it. Even within a lifetime, life can begin again.

Waking from the Dream

The world of dreams is such a wonderful place! That is, if you have love in your heart. If you have madness in your heart, you will have mad dreams. If you have guilt in your heart, you will have dreams that make you feel more guilt. But me, I have love in my heart and room for nothing else. I love my dreams and they love me.

Like all perennials in the universe, my season had come to an end. I lived there fourteen earth years. Kate and Luke lived long healthy lives. Immy and Joey lived there quite a long while too. Kate and Luke outlived several more dogs. A boy. A girl. A boy. A girl. They had some cats and a horse at one point. I could fill up a dozen more books with the story of the life they shared together. They had the normal ups and downs but they also experienced a love that transcended everything.

There were no secrets between them. One night they were reading her dream journal together and pondering the glimpses of the World Beyond and the meanings and the metaphors there. I will never forget when they got to the dream where I had jumped out of her car as a Bearded Collie Afghan Poodle and then, after a joyful run around the farmhouse, I was a Chocolate Lab. "Oh my God," they kept saying, "Oh my God!" when they realized the dream had come true. They laughed and they hugged and they cried when they realized that it was me. Immy and Joey were there on the big bed and they were wagging their tails, for they knew who I was when I was there. I wondered what it would have been like for us if she had realized it was me back then. But it doesn't matter. She loved me as Jack and she loved me as Jackie and I know in the blink of an eye she will know me again when she sees me again. She will love me again and again and again.

Not long after I passed from my life as Jackie, they adopted two small dogs named Salt and Pepper. I always get a kick out of those things, since I never told anyone that I used to call Luke "Salt and Pepper". It's a good example that shows that just the thought of something lives on long after you thought about it.

Everything we do in life is creating everything that's coming. Our thoughts and our words become things manifest in our lives. Each time my Master sent me to the right place at the right time. As promised, He has me in the right place right now.

She has worked through the grief and is full of love in her heart now too. It is bursting at the seams with the love she has learned in this lifetime. So anytime we meet in Dreamland, it is always a love story. In my dream now we are walking, she and I, together in the Rainbow Forest on Mulberry

Street. It is thick with trees and a rainbow carpet of heart-shaped leaves. We walk side by side. There is no leash. There is nothing else to do but walk together and love each other. We walk over to Grandfather Tree where he still stands tall and strong. She sits on the curve of his rooted trunk and pets me and we talk, my heart to hers and hers to mine...

...**SUDDENLY...**my awareness shifts. There is noise. Movement. Something is pulling me out of this trance. This dream. I don't want to leave. I don't want to leave her, but all too soon I am pulled back into the reality of the world I was in before I fell asleep...but wait. Am I awake? Am I asleep? I am not sure.

Wait. What IS that? Could it BE? I feel the vibration of her footstep on the threshold. The Rainbow Forest fades away from me, and Grandfather Tree and she does too, as I lift my head and open my eyes. A rainbow mist is all around.

I am on full alert. I feel, I smell, I hear, I sense, I love...and oh, I see! I see that she is HERE! Oh she is here! One foot in front of the other she comes closer and closer to me, over the Rainbow Bridge where I have been waiting for her. She starts out kind of slow because she has become quite old but by the time she reaches this side she will be just like the rest of us. The years will fade and she will be young again. My heart leaps. OH she is HERE!

270

I don't know how long I have been sleeping but I know that I am not dreaming now! So off I go, I don't waste another moment running to meet her at the edge of the Rainbow. It has been so long since I saw her face to face and yet not long at all. How could it be that I have lived a hundred lifetimes in a matter of moments?

I watch and wait intently. She doesn't see me yet. She is walking with the others. Lizard is right beside her and my friend the Hawk has already introduced himself to her. All my messenger friends are by her side, bringing her to me.

So many of us are lining up to greet her and welcome her home. Chuck, Grady and all the friends and loved ones from all the lifetimes shared. I am preparing for her for I am the one who loved her best. Luke loved her best too but he is not yet here so I get to be first in line! Just like my Master promised me a moment ago.

We think that we are living when we walk upon the earth but the very moment we "die" There, we wake up Here! This life on the other side of the Rainbow Bridge is the real one. We find that our life on earth was just a dream, a dream designed to lead us further and further into love. True love grows and then cannot be destroyed. It grows and grows until it is stronger than death.

I wait for her here at the edge of the rainbow. Every moment seems an hour. It reminds me of the life we shared on earth. She would come home from a long visit to

New York. I would hear her footstep and jump to attention, so excited to be together again. I would wait at the door of our house as I have waited at the edge of the Rainbow, for her to cross the threshold.

At last, it is the moment I have been dreaming of! It's the moment when her eyes meet mine...and nothing else exists for her or for me. Like a dream everything else fades away and all that exists is the love we share.

Oh she has arrived! I run and jump all over her just like the old times! Call me 'Jumping Jack' I don't care! All the rules go out the window when you love someone this much!

I hesitate one brief moment, for she is crying. Or is she laughing? Crying and laughing tears of joy because the joy we experience here is magnified tenfold and it cannot, will not be contained. The love we share envelops us and becomes everything we are and ever will be.

My earth master will soon meet my heavenly Master and she will see the one who coordinates all of these amazing lives for her for me for all of us. I can see Him from where we are and He is happy too. He looks at me smiling with his loving approval and His gentle heart speaks to mine.

"I told you so," He says. "I told you you'd be here in time to greet her." For this is what He dreamed of too and dreams always come true.

We are one and the same.
Your voice is my voice.
I call out to the canyon.
'I love you!'
My love for you fills the valleys
and the canyons;
All spaces are filled with my love for you.
Then the most amazing thing!
It echoes back.
All the love I feel for you
Comes back to me... comes back to me
Comes back to me
Comes back to me...
A never-ending song of love
For you and
For me.

Thank you for reading our book! If you enjoyed it, please consider giving us a rating or review.

If you grieve, be sure to read Jack's first book, "Reflections," which will walk you through the healing process.

Other links:
Jack's Facebook Support Group
www.Facebook.com/groups/EdgeoftheRainbow

Follow Jack on Facebook
www.facebook.com/MyJackofHearts

Read Jack's blog for regular posts about love and life and loss:
www.jackmcafghan.blogspot.com

Visit Kate at http://www.KateMcGahan.com where you can sign up, receive a free book and get author updates and helpful information.

With over 30 years of experience in hospice and eldercare, author Kate McGahan shares a wealth of knowledge based on her direct work with thousands of individuals and their families.

A graduate of Nazareth College of Rochester and Syracuse University, Kate is a Licensed Master of Social Work with a degree in Family Mental Health.

Combining natural intuition with the knowledge gained from her direct clinical practice, Kate seeks to entertain as well as to inspire each reader. She has a way of bringing her stories to her readers in a thought-provoking way. Her motto: Life Is The School Love is the Lesson. When you learn something new you can grow, when you grow you can heal and when you heal you can love. Read her books. You will never look at life or death or love the same way again.

Printed in Great Britain
by Amazon